Trips and Adventures

ACCOUNTS OF

Interesting and Varied Experiences

Compiled as Vol. II

OF THE

BOYS' AND GIRLS' FIRESIDE SERIES

By A. L. BYERS.

GOSPEL TRUMPET COMPANY
ANDERSON, IND.

PREFACE

The Boys and Girls' Fireside Series is an arrangement, in permanent form, of many excellent and interesting narratives, trips and adventures, little sermons, Bible stories, descriptions of nature, various industries and foreign customs, bits of biography and history, missionary experiences, little poems, etc., that have appeared from time to time in the SHINING LIGHT, a periodical for children. Comparatively few who are now in the transitory period of childhood have ever read them, and it is believed that in this permanent form they will be preserved as a treasure-store of useful reading in which boys and girls will find both pleasure and profit.

CONTENTS

TRIPS AND ADVENTURES

PURSUED BY WOLVES

IT WAS Saturday evening, and the last crimson rays of the sun were peering through the tall pines, spruces, cedars, tamaracks, birches, and maples that surrounded the logging-camp on Elk River in Wisconsin. Snow covered the ground. As the logging-crew, mostly Germans and Swedes, together with a few Americans, came into the camp, the sound of the woodsmen's axes and the clanking chains of the logging-sleds quieted for the day.

About forty workmen were engaged in the woods near by, cutting the trees and sawing the logs into lengths from twelve to eighteen feet. Others loaded the logs on the large sleds, by which the logs were conveyed three and a half miles to Long Lake. Here they were placed on the ice to await the warm weather of spring-time, when they were to be floated to the sawmill a mile distant. The sawmill was operated only in summer, to work up the timber cut the winter before, the average annual product being about two million feet.

Two large log houses, each about thirty feet wide and sixty feet long, composed the buildings of the camp. One was for the kitchen and the dining-room, while the other was filled with beds.

As a rule, the men were rough, and spent their spare time at camp in telling stories and playing cards, and even gambling to such an extent that their monthly pay was often lost almost as soon as they received it.

It was not the place for a boy of pure thoughts and ideals, as Emmet, who had always been taught by a Christian mother to live right. But during the winter the lumber-camp was about the only place where he could find employment in order to support his widowed mother and his brothers and sisters. Emmet had learned how to trust God, even while among those rough men, who lived very evil lives and profaned God's name with almost every expression.

When the week's work was done, happy thoughts of home filled Emmet's mind as he started out through the woods to his home a few miles away. The snow being deep and hard to travel through, dusk fell upon him about the time he reached Elk River, over which he was to cross in order to get home. Occasionally bears and large timber-wolves had been seen in this section, and the thoughts of some of the narrow escapes of which he had heard did not seem pleasant to a boy of seventeen years, who had no weapon with which to protect himself. The timber-wolves of this section usually stayed in the heavy under-brush.

As Emmet approached the river, his mind seemed to dwell upon what he would do were he to meet some of those ravenous wolves. As he descended the northern bank of the river, he perceived in the dim darkness two objects on the opposite side of the river. Thinking that these were wolves and that possibly they had not noticed him, he quietly stepped back under cover of the dense underbrush close to the river's edge. There Emmet looked up to his heavenly Father and asked for protection in this time of danger.

After a few minutes, thinking possibly the wolves had not seen him, he ventured upon the ice and started across. At first he stepped forth rather boldly, because at last sight of the beasts they were apparently going down the river on the opposite shore. He had not gone far, however, until one sly wolf came from the woods directly behind him, which showed that the beasts had crossed the river below and had come through the thick underbrush in order to attack him from behind.

It was now a great testing-time, and Emmet prayed again. The wolf approached within a few yards of the boy, then sat down, and, raising his nose high, made a loud, lonesome howl, which seemed to penetrate the surrounding forest with its wierd sound, and frightened Emmet greatly.

Suddenly the wolf returned to the woods, and Emmet continued his journey until he was about two thirds of the way across the ice. Then, looking over his shoulder, he saw two wolves coming very fast, and they continued to come until within a few rods. Standing still and eyeing the wolves, the boy raised a prayer to God. On this the wolves stopped coming, and, looking at the boy for a moment, threw up their heads and immediately ran across the river and disappeared in the darkness.

With a lighter heart and assurance of God's protecting care, Emmet continued the journey homeward, and with a thankful heart and conse-crated lips, he sang these words:

"My Jesus, I love thee,   My gracious Redeemer,
   I know thou art mine;   My Savior art thou;
For thee all the follies   If ever I loved thee,
   Of sin I resign.   My Jesus, 'tis now."

The lights of home shone from the windows upon the snow as Emmet came near, but little did the mother and the children realize the danger he had been in until he opened the door. They seemed to detect in his countenance something unusual. They all listened attentively while the entire story was related; then they thanked the Lord for the protection he had given in answer to prayer.

A BEAR STORY

THERE was once a little girl whose papa would often take her on his lap on stormy nights and tell her a true story of what had happened to him. And one time he told her a bear story.

One night when the thunder roared and the lightning flashed and the rain fell in torrents, he was out in the dark woods all alone, trying to find his way home. He could see only when the lightning flashed, and he walked on and on without knowing where he was wandering.

All at once, however, there was an unusually bright flash of lightning and he saw close by him some low bushes that looked as if they would shelter him from the rain, so he got down on his hands and knees and crept under them, and, to his surprize, found that he was in a small cave. He felt very glad to know that he was safe out of the storm.

But after a while, as he lay there, he heard something breathing heavily, and when the lightning flashed again he saw two bright eyes looking at him. Of course, he was frightened at first, but he was brave enough to strike a match, and there, near him, he saw a great big black bear. Bears are afraid of thunder and lightning, so this poor old fellow had crept into this cave to hide himself. When the man crept in the poor bear was probably glad to have him for company, for he did not try to hurt the man and did not even growl.

Morning came, the rain stopped, and the sun shone warm and bright. The man crawled out of the cave and so did the bear. When they both got out into the warm daylight, they stood and looked at each other.

If the man had struck at the bear or had run away from him, perhaps the bear would have attacked him and torn him, for he was very hungry and was, after all, a wild beast. But the man looked him straight in the eye and said gently, ''Well, old fellow, good morning!'' And the bear just gave a little grunt, as if saying, ''Good morning'' or ''Good-bye,'' and turned and trotted away.

In the clear daylight the man soon found his way home, and when he got there he told his little girl the true story of what had happened. And she liked it so much that she asks for the same story on every dark and stormy night.   —*Selected.*

AN EXPERIENCE WITH A DEVIL-FISH

A NUMBER of years ago some young men were staying at a resort on an island near the mouth of the Mississippi River. On one occasion these three young men went out rowing in the gulf waters about the island. Suddenly, as they passed along, they saw a large devil-fish near their boat. Now it happened that the boat which they had taken was one which was used in fishing. It contained a harpoon, which is a barbed spear attached to a long line and is used in capturing large fish.

As soon as they saw the devil-fish, they decided to harpoon it. So one of them threw the instrument, which sank deep into the body of the fish. Of course, this was great sport, and they were elated over the thought of capturing so large a devil-fish.

As soon as the fish was struck with the harpoon, it started swimming through the water and the line was soon all off the reel. Now, they were expecting that the fish would soon become exhausted and that then they would pull it safely to land. But the fish was larger and stronger than they had suspected, and when the line was all out of the boat, the fish pulled so hard that it almost pulled the bow of the boat beneath the water. And soon they realized that their boat was moving rapidly.

On and on they went, yet the fish did not slacken his speed or grow weary. They began to be somewhat alarmed, but it happened that there were several feet of chain on the end of the line that was fastened to the boat, so that there was no possibility of cutting loose from the fish.

Besides, it was also necessary that they all remain in the stern of the boat in order to keep the bow above the water.

They soon began to realize that they were in great danger, for they were traveling rapidly toward the center of the Gulf of Mexico, and were almost out of sight of land. Soon they lost sight of land, but still they traveled onward. Of course, there was nothing that they could do but to sit still and wait to see what would happen.

After about seven hours the fish managed to pull loose from the harpoon, but not until it had given the men a long ride on the gulf. They were glad when they found that the fish had gotten loose from their boat, but their troubles were not yet at an end. It was nearly night, and they realized that they were lost at sea. They were unable to tell the directions, and, of course, they knew that they could not live long without food or any fresh water to drink.

They were in great trouble and no doubt thought about their past sins and wickedness. Finally, darkness came and the night passed slowly by. When the sun rose next morning, they were still bewildered, and could see nothing but water and sky. All day they sat under the burning sun without food or drink, wondering what the end would be. Then, perhaps for the first time in life, these wicked young men thought of calling upon God, and in their distress they were humble enough even to plead with God to have mercy upon them.

Finally, on the third day, a large vessel came in sight. They signalled to the vessel for help. The captain of the ship saw them, and, knowing that they were lost, went to their rescue and took them on board his ship, which was bound for New Orleans.

They were, of course, very hungry, but the captain was wise enough not to give them all that they wanted to eat. All that he would let them have for the first time was a piece of dry bread called hardtack.

When they boarded the ship, they found that they were a few hundred miles out at sea, but the vessel sailed onward and brought them safe to land.

It was my privilege a few years ago, while I was traveling through the State of Mississippi, to make my home with one of these men for a short time. While I was with him he related to me this story.

—G. Q. Coplin.

THE LARGEST DEVIL-FISH EVER CAPTURED

A MONSTER devil-fish, eighteen feet long, and weighing 6,000 pounds, has been captured and killed off the southwest coast of Florida. It is now on exhibition in the Museum of Natural History, New York.

A 26-foot, open boat, with an eight-horse-power gasoline-engine was used in hunting this monster of the sea. In the boat were, besides the leader, a crew of five trained, native fishermen who were declared to be without fear. When the devil-fish was sighted, it might have escaped, but they do not fear men and boats. A huge lance, forged especially for this kind of hunting and three times as heavy as a whale-lance, was used. Soon after the boat, followed by a heavy timber-drag, passed through the Captive Inlet into the waters of the Gulf, the monster was sighted, and immediately the harpoon was driven into its back. Being now fast to the drag, the fish fought a desperate battle with the men in the boat, which lasted only twenty-two minutes, after which the dead devil-fish, when examined, showed just twenty-three wounds. The wonderful vitality of these creatures is proved by the fact that many of them have fought and gained their freedom after being harpooned, lanced, and shot through many times with heavy caliber rifles.

The devil-fish is black, and it has a thick, short, rigid tail and a number of fins. It also has a formidable array of large, flat teeth, well adapted to their owner's needs.

LOST IN THE WILDS

N ORTHWESTERN Wisconsin, not a great many years ago, had heavy pine forests covering thousands of acres. A man could travel for many miles and not see houses, fences, or even roads. But at the time of my story, the pine had been cut off and the land was being sold for farms.

One morning in November two boys, one eleven years old and the other thirteen, started out in this wilderness to hunt for a cow that had strayed away. They took their dinner along, as they expected to be gone all day. At first everything went well. When they grew hungry, they sat down under a bridge and ate their lunch. After lunch they were ready to start out again, but neither could tell from which direction they had come. They finally agreed on the direction and decided to go home.

They followed the road they had found, which happened to be an old logging road and which became poorer the farther they went. Finally it ended, but they were so sure they were on the way home that they decided to take a short cut. "Just a little way is the sawmill; then we shall be pretty near home," they said. But they had not gone far before they found out that they were lost. It soon grew dark. Once they thought they could hear a dog bark, and they began to call for help as loudly as they could. The answer they got was a fierce growl from some wild animal, which scared them so they ran as fast as they could run. Shortly after dark they heard wolves begin to howl, and they could even hear animals walking in the brush.

Poor boys! Their feet were wet and cold, but they had no way to dry and warm them; they were tired and sleepy, but they dared not lie down to sleep. What a long night that must have been for these boys! It was about three o'clock in the afternoon of the next day before they found a road. A man with a team overtook them and gave them a ride. They asked him the way home, but he did not know there was such a place as they asked for. So they inquired at the first house they came to and were told that they were eighteen miles from home and going still farther away.

When the boys learned this, they quickly decided to start in the right direction. But it was so near night that the farmer would not let them go; he invited them to remain all night. The next morning they started for home, arriving there about two o'clock in the afternoon. Their mother had given up all hope of ever seeing her boys again; for they had been away two whole nights and nearly three days. When she saw them, she could hardly believe her eyes; she could scarcely control herself for joy. Surely she was very thankful to the Lord for protecting them amid wild animals. One of these boys, in speaking of this incident after he became a man, said, "That was an experience I shall never forget."   —*G. Louis Welling.*

A VISIT TO MAMMOTH CAVE

TWO days' traveling by automobile in Kentucky brought us to Cave City. This town is ten miles from the noted Mammoth Cave. We had previously planned to visit this wonderful place and were now anxiously waiting till we should arrive there. The ten miles of road that led to the cave were as bad roads as we had to pass over during our whole journey. We were afraid our machine would break, but we were spared this trouble. A girl friend accompanied us from Cave City.

It was dark when we arrived at the cave. Half-past seven was the appointed time for parties to start on the night trip. Having two hours to wait, we purchased our tickets and then went into a room in the large hotel and interested ourselves by looking at the many views and souvenirs of the cave. When at last the hour arrived, a party of eight was waiting at the gate where a path leads to the entrance.

Our guide was a very interesting man. He was fifty years of age. He had spent thirty-five years exploring this cave, and he knows of many places in there that no other man has ever seen. He has explored to the distance of one hundred and fifty miles. His recent discovery is "Violet City," so named because of its beauty.

The mouth of the cave is about fifty feet wide and twenty feet high. After entering, we descended probably one hundred fifty steps. We noticed a stream of water falling from the top of the mouth, and as it fell it disappeared in the ground. As we took our last look at the stars and descended farther into the cave, a chilly feeling crept over us. We began to realize that we were going into a wonderful place in the earth. The passage that led to the cave proper became smaller until we came to an iron fence, in which was a little iron gate. This our guide unlocked; we walked through; and he locked it again. Now we turned our faces inward. Some one said, "Look! What are those dark bunches hanging to the ceiling?" Our guide told us they were bats. At this place we could almost touch the ceiling, and on examination we found dozens of bats all huddled together. As winter comes on, we were told, they go farther into the cave, but when spring comes they gradually go to the outside.

The farther we descended, the higher became the arch above us until we came to a very large room, or hall. Here it was as warm as anywhere in the cave. The temperature in the cave, by the way, never varies the year round. The cave is said to breathe twice a year; that is, the draft of air blows inward for six months, and during the other six it blows outward.

We left all our wraps and everything that might hinder us in walking, in a little square, tight house. These were made secure so that we might find our buttons still on and no holes in our pockets, for the cave-rats seem to delight in such behavior as mutilating garments. Most of us had oil-torches.

One of the first things we noticed was the hardness of the ground. Although thousands of people visit this place every year, yet there is very little dust. We saw distinct tracks of oxen, made in 1812. Perhaps you wonder how these tracks came to be here. In the war of 1812 there was need of saltpeter with which to make gunpowder. As there was much saltpeter in the earth of this cave, arrangements were made to secure it. Large vats, or pits, were made, into which the earth was thrown. Large pipes, made of logs twenty feet long with four-inch holes through them, carried water in to soak the saltpeter out of the earth. The water was pumped out by hand through other pipes. Ruins of these pipes and vats are still there. This was done in the first half mile of the cave.

We followed close to our guide, ever on the watch for holes or pits. We were shown one pit called the Bottomless Pit, so named because of its great depth. Our guide threw a piece of burning oiled waste down into it so that we could see the bottom. On both sides of our path were great piles of small pieces of stone. On inquiring, we found them to be stones piled up by people from different States, colleges, leagues, and lodges, each pile representing a State, etc. My sister and I put on stones for Indiana and Alabama.

As we went along, our guide would occasionally throw some burning oiled waste upon a ledge or overhanging rock that we might better see above us. It was black darkness in there except for the light of our small torches. Sometimes he would light a tape that made a white light. He would also light a fuse on a little thing that would explode and burn. This illuminated the walls beautifully. At one place the large hall, or street, made two distinct turns. This street was called Broadway.

At different places along the way certain images were pictured on the walls. One was the picture of a kitten lying down, another a giant and giantess tossing their baby to each other. One large rock viewed from a certain point looked like a huge coffin made for a giant. This was called the Giant's Coffin. Once our guide bade us be quiet. While listening, we could hear a distinct "tick-tock, tick-tock" like the sound of a clock. He explained to us that is was the continual dropping of water from the rock above into a pool below.

Soon we came to some houses made of the stones of the cave. These were built a number of years ago. Physicians thought that an even temperature was very essential to the recovery of consumptives. Nearly a dozen men who were consumptives were taken into this cave to see if the even temperature would help them. No doubt, you can guess the result of keeping such men where the sunlight never penetrates and the air is very heavy. Most of them died in a few months. The remaining few were taken out, but all died on the way out except one, and he died before he reached the hotel. The sudden change of temperature was too much for them. These stone houses were built for their use while in there.

Farther on to the left we came to what is called the Methodist Church, and a short distance on to the right of Broadway was the Theater. The guide then showed us the back way to the Methodist Church. He said jokingly that bad boys would slip out of church the back way and go to the theater.

One place in the ceiling is called the Egg Chamber, because there is the natural shape of an immense egg, probably fifty feet long.

As we traveled on down Broadway, passing many things of interest, we finally came to the Bridal Altar. This is formed of stalactites and stalagmites that have united, forming pillars. These vary in diameter from six inches to one foot. The ground at this place is somewhat elevated. It was so named because it suggested a bridal altar.

A story is told of the first wedding at this altar, as follows: A certain mother did not want her daughter ever to marry. The daughter promised the mother she would never marry a man on the face of the earth. But the time came when the daughter became acquainted with a worthy man who she thought would be a suitable life companion. So in order to be true to her promise, she and her betrothed went down to this altar in the cave and were married. Thus she did not marry a man on the face of the earth. I can not say that this story is true, but it has been told to many people. A considerable number of weddings have taken place here under the earth. A wedding had occurred just a few days before we were there. Some of the decorations still remained.

We passed on, seeing one thing after another at which we looked in wonder. At last we came to some seats, on which our guide bade us be seated. This was a welcome invitation, and we sat down, setting our torches out in front of us. The guide came along and picked them up, saying that he would relieve us of their unpleasant odor.

He was a droll fellow, and at times we could hardly tell whether he meant just what he said or not. You can imagine our feelings when he began to talk somewhat after this fashion: "Well, I didn't want to come tonight. It was tired and wanted to spend the evening with my family. But I was ordered to guide you through here, so I had to come. But now you've seen some of the cave, and as I have the torches already in my hands and can go much faster without you, I'll just strike out for home. Good-by. I'll see you in the morning.''

And off he went with every light. He started down to one story below us, and we sat there not knowing what would happen next. I can tell you that some startling thoughts flashed through our minds. But our suspense was relieved somewhat when, after he had descended some distance, he told us to look up. Above us we beheld what looked very much like the starry heavens. We were in the Starry Chamber. He then let a shadow, representing a cloud, pass over it and off again, after which the stars appeared much brighter. Of course, it was not the cloud that made them appear brighter; the change was in our eyes. ''Now,'' he said, ''good-by for the last time. I'll see you in the morning.'' So he went down through an under passage till we could not see a ray of light in any direction.

Oh, how dark it was! We talked with each other and wondered whether our guide would come back and what we should do if he did not. One man said he would not stay in there twenty-four hours alone for a thousand dollars. I am quite sure the thought of eternity came to us all. The darkness reminded me of the scripture, ''To whom is reserved the blackness of darkness forever.''

My father suggested that it was a good time to pray, a remark which made a strong impression, for nothing was said for some time. I could not tell how long we sat there; it seemed a good while, but probably it was not so long as we imagined. Then suddenly we saw a faint streak of red light on the walls of the cave far in the distance. Then we heard a sound like a rooster crowing. The light became brighter, reminding us of the sunrise, till our guide and his lights came in view. Then he called out, ''Good-morning! The sun's up.''

Some of the girls had been asking for some water to drink, and he had told them that there was not to be any pools of water on this trip; but after he came back he said that as they so much desired water he would take us to a pool not far away. So we followed him, and he went straight toward the solid wall. But there was an opening in that wall just wide enough for us to pass through, one at a time. It was fifty feet high and at least two rods through. We descended until we came to another room in which the ceiling was very low. We could almost touch it at places with our heads, and the water was seeping down through this ceiling all the time. We passed a pit, where we were warned to be careful, and then we came to a pool of water. There was an indentation about four feet across and two feet deep. The water stood eight or ten inches deep all the time. We all gathered around the edge. The guide stepped down and with a dipper gave us each some water to drink. As we were thirsty, we very much appreciated this good, cool, clear water. After we had finished, he told us the pool was the Devil's Bathing Pool. And we all had a good laugh.

Some one wanted to look into the pit we were warned to keep away from; so the guide took us over, and we looked into a very deep hole. It is called Joseph's Pit. We were led back through the crevice to where we had been sitting.

We then began to retrace our steps. We went back a long distance till we came near to two square turns in Broadway. Here were some benches. We sat on these but kept our lights. Our guide went on ahead of us past the turns quite a distance. Then he lighted a white light and called to us. We stood at a certain place where he had shown us and looked toward him. We saw an immense statue of Martha Washington. When we stood at a certain angle, the image was very natural; but if we changed to either side, it was not natural. This statue was formed by the white light shining past the corners of those two turns in the street. After looking at this for some time, we went to where our guide was waiting for us.

We soon came to a place where our guide turned into an avenue leaving Broadway. Then we came to the great armchair. This was another formation of stalactites and stalagmites. We took turns in sitting in the chair and then passed on. Presently we came where it was a little muddy. Here water was seeping down through the ceiling and dropping on stones below, which were worn smooth and round. One stone looked very much like a man's face, front view.

We then began to ascend. Up, up we went till we came so close to the top that we had to bend over, and the passage was narrow. Back in there we came to a shallow pit which had a fence around it. Here were many small stalactites and stalagmites forming. These were the only small ones that we could see on our trip. All others had been broken off by visitors years before this to take away as souvenirs.

Perhaps you have been wondering what stalactites and stalagmites are. A stalactite begins to form by drops of water containing a certain amount of mineral substance seeping through the ceiling. These drops (if they do not come too fast) will evaporate, each leaving a little more mineral to harden, and in this way a small icicle in appearance is gradually formed. A stalagmite is about the same, only it grows from the ground up by little drops of water dropping off the stalactite. The stalactites and stalagmites grow very gradually toward each other until finally they meet and grow together. The columns so formed our guide called "mightytites." These icicle-like forms grow in length one hundredth of an inch every year, or one inch in one hundred years. At this pit many of these stalactites and stalagmites were forming. They varied in size from that of a drop of water to four feet long. We then returned to Broadway.

As we were walking along, our guide was telling us about the cavecrickets. Of course, we wanted to see some; so he led us up and out to an overhanging rock close to the ceiling. There they were. They looked like white crickets. They had feelers four inches long or four times the length of their bodies. While at this place, we wrote our names on the ceiling, as thousands had done before us. It was not long then until we came to the little house where our wraps had been placed. When we started to ascend the 150 steps to the entrance, we began to notice our tired limbs more than ever. It was eleven o'clock when we reached the hotel, but we felt fully repaid for our five-mile walk.

—*Opal Smith.*

IN THE CANADIAN ROCKIES
The Railroad Journey

A LONG railroad journey was before us. Omitting a description of the first part of our trip, I shall begin at St. Paul, where we boarded a magnificent Soo-Pacific train, which should bear us many hundreds of miles away. There were ten coaches, including two tourist-cars, in one of which we had engaged a section by telegraph before leaving home.

Tourist-cars are built like standard sleepers, but are not finished quite so expensively. They are intended to accommodate the many tourists who, having reduced-rate tickets, wish to have their sleeping accommodations also less expensive. One has to pay extra to ride in a sleeper, but only about half as much for a tourist as for a standard. In the Soo-Pacific service, the tourist sleepers are finished in mahogany and are upholstered in leather or rattan. They are roomy, airy, and probably more sanitary than the standards, which have heavier upholstering.

The interior of a sleeping-car is divided into sections, each consisting of two seats facing each other. In daytime the appearance is not much different from that of the ordinary day-coach; but if you were to look into one at night, you would not know it was the same car. The aisle has become a narrow hall, walled with curtains, and each section has become a little bedroom with two beds, or berths, one above the other. The porter has made up the beds with nice clean pillows and bed-clothing, and has turned the lights low, and all is quiet save the dull rumbling of the wheels beneath.

Thus, we see these cars are private. They are occupied by people who go long distances and have their own sections, or berths, which they have paid for. People are not getting on and off at every station, as with a common day-coach. There are toilet-rooms where one may wash; and in one end of the car is a little room containing a stove, on which a lunch may be warmed or food may be cooked. Pleasant acquaintances are formed, and one feels quite at home; the truth is, one may travel for two or three days and be loath to leave his tourist-car.

By the time we were comfortably settled in our sections, we were speeding over a smooth roadbed in a northwesterly direction, across the prairies and past the lakes of Minnesota. Ahead of us, in the Dakotas and in Canada, were hundreds of miles of prairie, where the signs of habitation, the little sod houses, were few and far between. There were great fields of wheat, barley, and flax. We would see wild flowers, sage-bushes, and sometimes prairie dogs or coyotes. There were great stretches of new country, where occasionally would be seen a traction-plow turning the sod for the first time.

About 4 P. M., in western Minnesota, our train, which had been running on time, came to a standstill out in the open country. As it did not proceed, we alighted to see what was the matter. A glance up the track soon revealed the trouble. A half mile ahead was a long, wrecked freight-train. Something went wrong with the trucks of one of the forward cars, which caused the train to buckle, some of the cars to shoot off to the right, and others to the left. About a dozen cars

were badly smashed, and their contents scattered about. Machinery, cement, ladies' shoes, candy, beer, giant firecrackers, and other miscellaneous articles lay in great confusion.

As the track was torn up, and this wreck was in the way, our train could go no further. After waiting for some time, perhaps for orders, our train ran backwards about fifty miles to Glenwood, where the Soo Line branches north to Winnipeg, then made a detour by the way of Fargo and the Northern Pacific, reaching our own line again at Valley City. After the train started backwards from the wreck, evening drew on and we took our berths. It was our first night in a tourist-car, and it did not matter whether we were going forwards or backwards, we slept soundly. Morning found us crossing the river at Fargo. There are many wrecks in life that are not so easily gotten around as was this one.

The next day we reached the boundary-line at Portal, where there were two stations close together, one in the United States and the other in Canada. Over one was hoisted the American flag and over the other the British. A red metal post marks the boundary-line. As I had never been out of my native country, it was an eventful moment when I approached the line, paused, and then stepped over.

The customs officials had boarded our train and inspected our baggage, and we were soon on our way again. We spent one more night and a day before reaching Banff. We were due there at 9:45 A. M. of the third day, but on account of the wreck in Minnesota we were seven hours late and did not arrive till 5 P. M. (seventeen o'clock by the Canadian Pacific system of reckoning time in Western Canada).

Here we were in the mountains of Canada, 1,250 miles from St. Paul. We were not in the least tired of our trip.

We were anxious to get a view of the Rockies from a distance of a hundred miles or so, but it happened that the air was laden with mist, which obstructed our view. So we did not see the mountains until we were right among them and had to stoop low to see their tops through the car-windows.

Here we were, sure enough, in a land of snow-capped, cloud-piercing mountains; a land of jutting crags and majestic glaciers; a land of beautiful cascades and of dashing, roaring streams; of clear, quiet lakes and of scenic valleys flanked with evergreen forests. To see the patches of snow on the heights above us, and to feel the corresponding cold, was something we were not accustomed to in the latter part of June.

Banff and the Bow River

Banff is in Alberta, just east of the Great Divide; for as yet we had not reached the highest ridge, or crest, of the Rockies. The Bow River is a swift-gliding stream which, a short distance below the village, forms a rapids so steep as to be called the Bow Falls.

We spent the first day viewing the wonders of God's creation. The Christian can enjoy these wonders more than those who know not God, for he feels that these things are the handiwork of his own dear Father.

After viewing the Falls a while we proceeded up the slope of Sulphur Mountain, to a point where we had the view of the Bow Valley exactly as shown in the picture. On this mountain are springs of sulphur water, warm from the internal heat of the earth. This water is conducted into bathing-pools. To take a plunge into one of these is a benefit as well as a treat.

The Rocky Mountains are more rugged and snowy in Canada than farther south. Their sides up to a high altitude are covered with evergreen forests of pine, spruce, fir, and other woods, which scent the air with their odor. The snow-patches, melting at their lower edges, become the sources of little streams, which dash rapidly down their rocky courses to the lower levels, where they unite and gain a considerable size. The roaring of these streams is a familiar sound in these forests. The stones they encounter keep them lashed into foam, which gives them a white appearance. The water is well aired, and is always clear, pure, and cold.

Imagine, then, the grandeur of these mountains—their barren, rugged summits flecked with snow, and so high that the clouds frequently play about them; their sides clothed with green and streaked with the silver of the streams! Behold, what sublime and awesome scenes! Must

there not have been a terrific breaking of the earth's crust when, in the long ago, these mountains were thrown upward to the skies? What a mighty God we serve! and how wonderful is his handiwork!

The Great Divide

The Rocky Mountains are the highest ridge of land between the Pacific Ocean on the west and the Mississippi River, or, we may say, the Atlantic Ocean, on the east. Thus they are sometimes called the backbone of the continent. The Rocky Mountains in Canada are not one uniform ridge of land, but consist of broken, irregular ridges, with valleys and streams between. The railroads, in crossing a range, do not run up to the tops of the high mountains. They run in the valleys and follow upward along the streams until they are compelled to strike directly across the crest, or ridge, which forms the watershed of the range. This crossing-place is called a pass; and though it is the lowest and most convenient point the railroad can find, it is also the highest point on the line, and it requires two or more engines to draw a train up to this point. On account of its being the watershed, from which the streams flow in opposite directions, the highest range is called the Great Divide.

The pass where the Canadian Pacific Railroad crosses the Great Divide is called the Kicking Horse Pass. The highest point in the road is easily discerned and shows plainly in a long freight-train, for the car that is on the ridge is easily seen to be higher than the rest.

Directly on top of this ridge is a little stream, which divides, sending one half of its waters to the Atlantic and the other half to the Pacific. One branch turns eastward into the Bow River, which empties into the Saskatchewan, and that in turn into Hudson Bay; while the other branch turns westward into the Kicking Horse River, which empties into the Columbia, and that in turn into the Pacific. It was interesting to fill our drinking-cup and send its contents to the Atlantic or to the Pacific, just as we chose.

This Great Divide also forms the boundary between the provinces of Alberta and British Columbia. Here also stands a monument to Sir James Hector, who in 1858 discovered this pass.

Just beyond the Great Divide, and before Field is reached, is a wonderful piece of engineering. Formerly the railroad was so steep that four engines were required to bring a train up from the west. Now is requires but two. The road has been lenghtened four and one fourth miles and the grade, or steepness, is correspondingly lessened. How was it done? By tunneling into the mountain on either side and describing a letter S instead of running straight. In going down from the Divide the road turns into one mountain, describes a circle, and comes out lower down; then, crossing the valley, enters the opposite mountain, makes a circle, and comes out still lower down; then continues on down the valley. Thus, there are two circular tunnels, together one and one fourth miles in length. This work cost one and one half million dollars, and required one thousand men for twenty months, and the use of seventy-five carloads of dynamite.

From the Great Divide we continued our journey to Field, a village nestled against Mt. Stephen. We had heard of the fossil-beds on this mountain; so we climbed to where they were, about halfway up the

rather steep slope, near the spot marked by a small cross in the picture. We gathered a number of fossils of trilobites. These were crustaceans of the Paleozoic time, and were therefore among the very earliest forms of life. They lived in the water, and therefore at a time before the mountains were yet thrown up. In the mountains one can plainly see the layers, or strata, of the rocks that were pushed upward when the mountains were formed. Sometimes these strata are nearly level; but generally they incline. Those on the east of the Divide incline in an opposite direction from those on the west, just as the layers of a cake would appear if the cake were broken by being pushed upward from below.

Roughing It

The day we spent at Banff was Sunday. On Monday morning we donned our rough clothing, including our big high-top boots, and prepared to spend about ten days following trails, climbing mountains, wading snow-banks and streams, clambering over rocks, etc. Our purses were not suited to the expensive railway hotels, and having a trunk well filled with provisions, we decided to take care of ourselves as best we could. We had canned goods, dried beef, nuts, and sundry others things. For bread we were to be satisfied with biscuit-crackers and hardtack (or, as Charles, our Southern friend, was disposed to pronounce it without the "r," "ha'd tack").

We had a few blankets, some of which were ponchos and would turn water. Also, we had not omitted a compass, hatchet, kodak, telescope (spy-glass), whistles, and hunting-knives. We were not allowed to carry firearms without hunting licenses, and these for foreigners were too expensive to obtain. Besides, this region had been reserved as the Canadian National Park, and we were not supposed to kill any animals. However, we carried our knives.

We first climbed to the top of Sulphur Mountain, whose height is only 8,000 feet. An easy trail led to the summit. To reach the tops of mountains these trails zigzag through evergreen forests until one gets to the timber-line (above which trees do not grow). For the rest of the way the trail leads among rocks, or over them; for these mountains are well named Rocky Mountains.

In the park at Banff we took particular notice of a monstrous mountain-lion, which paced from corner to corner of his cage. Also we sized up the grizzly, as this animal was our principal bugaboo while in the mountains, though it happened we never saw one wild.

There will not be space to tell of our mountain-tramping in detail. We stopped at four different stations: Banff, Laggan (now called Lake Louise), Field, and Glacier, each of which in turn we made the base from which to explore the surrounding region.

From Laggan we visited the Lakes in the Clouds, which, though more than a mile above sea-level, nestle among mountains that rise thousands of feet still higher above them. Some of these lakes are exceedingly beautiful. The smallest and highest of these, Lake Agnes, is shown in the picture lying to the right of Beehive and in front of Pope's Peak. From this lake we ascended the easy slope of Beehive to the point marked in the picture by a small cross. Here we ate our lunch, right at the edge of the eastern side, which drops almost perpendicularly for a thousand feet. A foot or two further, and we would have fallen off. The situation was a little frightful, but we banished

all fear and felt just as safe as if we had been further from the edge.

At a secluded spot in the woods, near the shore of Lake Louise, we constructed a rude tent. We cut a ridge-pole and cross poles, and pinned two of our poncho-blankets together for a roof. The rear end was against a tree, and some brush. We built a fire with which to warm our victuals. The green fir-boughs, containing pitch, burn easily. We cut a quantity of boughs and placed them in order for our bed, then spread over them our third poncho, and lastly our blankets and quilts.

We had pillows, and altogether, when everything was arranged, our rude home did not look uninviting. We had battled through discouragements and began to think of some comfort for the night. The mosquitoes, which had attacked us furiously, settled as the coolness of the night drew on. We thought of how it pays to go right through discouragements instead of giving up to them. There is always something that rewards perseverance.

Here we were to spend the night in the woods. Dan, the first to get under the covers, crawled back to the rear. My turn came next; and Charles, up to this time unmindful that if a bear came to eat us it would get him first, was compelled to lie in front, and he placed his knife at his pillow. How did we rest? Why, the best we could with three in a bed and the covers too narrow to cover us comfortably. The one in the middle was not concerned in the tug of war between the outside parties for keeping the cover from slipping over to the other fellow and leaving number one in the cold. But the middle man had to take the squeezing. The cover was always tightly stretched. This was our experience whenever we slept together. When we could do so, we managed to sleep in some boarding-house near the station. Once we spent the night with a section foreman in his shanty.

Glaciers and Waterfalls

I have already spoken of the snow-patches on the mountains as they appear in summer. The snow, of course, is lodged more deeply in the ravines and in the hollows between the peaks where the heads of the valleys are formed. Ordinarily these snow-patches are small and not very deep. But there are places where the snow-field is large, and where in the hollows or valleys between the peaks the snow accumulates to such a depth and weight that it is pressed into a form of ice. The more this keeps thawing and freezing the more icelike and slippery it becomes. The whole mass by its own weight and by the changing effects of heat and cold, as well as by the pressure of fresh snows above, gradually slides downward into the valley. Such a descending mass of snow and ice is called a glacier.

As fast as a glacier slides downward it melts off at the foot, so that it never gets very far down. For some reason glaciers do not extend so far down into the valleys as they formerly did. Perhaps the climate is warmer and they therefore melt off farther up at the foot. Glaciers

move very slowly, some not more than an inch a day; others move two or three feet in one day. They contain great crevasses, or cracks, and men have fallen into these and never gotten out again. Of course they froze to death. It is very dangerous to climb over a glacier, especially after a fresh snow has closed some of the cracks so that one can not see and avoid them.

The picture shows a glacier that is located only a short distance from the station called Glacier, on the Canadian Pacific Railroad. Charles and I attempted to climb up the rocks beside this glacier to the snow-field above. Once we became separated for a short time, and when I whistled repeatedly there was no answer. Imagine my feelings

when I thought he must have lost his hold and tumbled down the rocks to almost certain death. But soon I saw him away above me. He had taken a shorter and more dangerous route than I, and the wind had hindered his hearing my call. We thought best not to continue to the crest of the glacier as night was coming on, and we had some dangerous places to descend, also we might not find our trail.

After we had left the glacier and were following the trail back to the station, I noticed a porcupine running slowly three or four rods ahead of me. He did not seem to be frightened, and allowed me to run up to him. I knew he was covered with sharp spines, but as I had on buck-skin gloves, I grabbed him by the tail just as he turned off the path into the bushes. But I had no sooner closed my hand on his tail than I opened it again. My thumb and fingers were sticking full of spines, sharper than needles. I concluded never to take hold of a porcupine again, even if I had on buckskin gloves.

The melting snows and glaciers in the upper regions become the sourc-es of numerous streams. I have al-ready described how these streams come tumbling and roaring down the mountains. Sometimes they fall over precipices of great height, and. form cascades, or waterfalls. These streams pouring over great heights and almost losing them-selves in mist before they reach the rocks below, are a very common and interesting sigh t in the Canadian Rockies. Takakkaw Falls is a noted cataract in this region. It is about twelve miles up the Yoho Valley from Field. Charles and I con-cluded we would visit these falls. Our friend Dan, deciding not to make the trip, remained at our lodging-house. We left the village on the afternoon of July 1, and took a four-teen-mile route to the falls, by way of the Natural Bridge and Emerald Lake. We spent the night on the shore of Emerald Lake and the next morning resumed our course, which led over the mountain and through mud and snowbanks to the falls. We could hear the roar of the falls before we could see them. Finally they burst on our view just as they are shown in the picture. The water falls 1,200 feet, and it is a sight worth traveling to see. Note the glacier lying on the heights above the falls.

We returned by way of the Yoho Valley, which has some of the most beautiful scenery that one can imagine. We were a little footsore, but not very weary, as one does not tire easily in the cool, bracing atmosphere of the mountains.

After ten days of this kind of adventure in the mountains of Canada we journeyed westward to the Pacific Coast.   —*A. L. Byers.*

EXPERIENCE WITH A PANTHER

THERE was once related to me an incident of a young man who was in the habit of going late to meeting. He did not go for the good he might get out of the meeting, but "just to be going" and to ride home with his companions. As he was riding along slowly, he thought he heard a cry like that of a little child in distress. His pony began to grow uneasy and want to run, but he held her back; he was listening to the cries which seemed to come nearer.

For some time the thought did not occur to him that he was in danger; when finally he realized his situation and started to run, the panther gave a great scream, and he heard her claws scratch the fence as she must have leaped toward him. As the pony was swift he escaped without injury.

When he returned, he was in company with several others who had been at the meeting. They neither saw nor heard anything of the panther, as panthers do not attack one unless he is alone.

Many parts of this story remind me of the way the devil tries to capture souls. He sees them going carelessly or listlessly along, and he begins little by little to entice them to him and his ways. Some are drawn to him by his deception, even if conscience does become troubled and wants to carry its owner away from the allurement (1 Thess. 5:22).

Should others see their dangerous position and try to escape, he makes a great effort to prevent them, perhaps a great noise to scare; but we need not be taken if we flee to the refuge in Christ Jesus.
            —*Frances Jones Dodge.*

A TRIP UP THE COLUMBIA

NO RIVER voyage in the United States could be more interesting and more full of scenic wealth than a voyage through the Cascade Mountains on the bosom of the matchless Columbia. We had been in Portland but a day or two when, at seven o'clock on a morning in July, we boarded the Bailey Gatzert for The Dalles, over one hundred miles up the river.

Portland is not on the Columbia, however, but on the Willamette. As we proceeded down the latter stream to its mouth, a strong col:l

wind was blowing. We persisted in remaining on the upper deck, and eagerly sought the places that were sunny or sheltered from the wind. Soon our steamer turned her bow to the right, and headed up the Columbia.

There was not much of special interest in the first part of the voyage; but on ahead was a splendid panorama of frowning promontories, curiously-formed rocks, beautiful water-falls, gorges, bluffs, and distant views of snowy peaks. Tall straight sides of the mountains rose, in some cases, from the very edge of the river. For a long distance the course of the river is one vast gorge. On each side of the river is a railroad, and the passing trains running along the banks above the water's edge, and plunging into and out of the tunneled rocks, kept us company.

The rock called Cigar Rock is one of the many curious formations, which are usually named from their shape. Thus there are Rooster Rock, the Pillars of Hercules, Cape Horn, and Castle Rock. The last named is 1,146 feet high and was formerly a lookout station for the Indians. Until 1901 its summit had never been scaled by a white man.

Latourelle Falls is an example of the beautiful waterfalls that may be seen from the steamer. Multunomah Falls appears as a filmy veil of lace, falling 720 feet into a basin on the hillside, and then 130 feet further into the river. Oneonta Gorge is a huge, rock-riven cleft, its sides covered with mosses, vines, and ferns.

One thing of special interest was the Cascade Locks. The steamer would enter the locks, and then the gates behind would close. If the steamer was going up-stream, the water would be turned in from above, until the steamer, thus elevated to the level of the water ahead, could proceed. In returning down stream, the process would be reversed. The water would be left to run out of the locks until the lower level was reached. Wherever there are canals there usually have to be some locks. Perhaps some of the readers have seen boats pass through locks.

At 3 P. M. we reached The Dalles, our farthest point up-stream. The Dalles is a pretty little town nestling among the hills. It was formerly a fur-trading station, and a favorite resort of the Indians, for it was the best place in the Columbia to spear salmon. Further than The Dalles our steamer could not go, for there were obstructions such as may be seen in the picture. The government has since improved the Upper Columbia, and opened it to navigation, having spent millions of dollars in the undertaking.

There is another thing which one sees on the Columbia, and which interests people who have never seen the like before, and that is the fish-wheels. Salmon abound in the Columbia. A huge wheel, the lower part of which is submerged in the water, turns vertically by the force of the current. It is equipped with screen buckets, or pockets. As the wheel turns, these dip into the water, and if a fish happens to get into one, it is lifted up as the wheel turns and is dropped into a slide, or chute, and landed in the place prepared to receive it. Thus a fish-wheel catches the fish, and lands them, all by the force of the current.

On the return down stream we had a chance to see the second time what we had seen going up-stream. Finally, as night dropped her mantle at the close of the day, we landed at the Portland docks; but the beauties of Nature's wonders seen that day will ever remain in the vision of our imagination.   —A. L. Byers.

CLIMBING MOUNT HOOD

MOUNT HOOD is one of the mountain peaks I had to locate in the geography class when a schoolboy. Through the kindness of a friend, Timmons, with whom we were staying in Portland, Ore., it was my privilege to visit Mount Hood and climb to its summit. It is situated in northern Oregon, about twenty-five miles south of the Co-

lumbia River and fifty-six miles east of Portland. I had gotten a view
of it from Portland, also while on our trip up the Columbia.

The mountain is of volcanic origin, and therefore is unlike the Rockies. Hood stands by itself, a distinct cone, built up of flowing lava
when its crater belched out fire, smoke, and lava in the distant past.
The soil for many miles around these old volcanoes is lava soil. There
is a place near the summit where sulphur fumes are still escaping.

We left Portland on a morning in the latter part of July. There
were four of us including Timmons, who was taking us in his automobile. The ride across the country we very much enjoyed. We stopped
at a farmhouse and picked some large, sweet cherries, paying only

four cents a quart for them. These we ate along the way. We had to
stop a number of times and cool the engine. As we approached the
mountain and were going almost constantly up-grade, our machine became heated, and then our progress was slow. Night overtook us near
the base of the mountain.

We camped beside a creek. Arranging our blankets for beds and
taking our seat-cushoins for pillows, we lay down in God's great out-
of-doors, in a region infested with bears and cougars. These we did
not fear; but one species of God's creation gave us much trouble, and
that was mosquitoes. I slept but little that night. In the morning as
we made preparations to start, we were each surrounded by a swarm
of mosquitoes. We were glad enough to pull out of there. Soon we

arrived at Government Camp, where we learned that the place where we camped was called Mosquito Creek, the very worst place to camp.

But we felt that in a general way God had prospered us, for here we were at the base of Mount Hood, ready for what experiences were ours to enjoy or endure. The distance to the summit was eight miles. As our eyes scanned its slopes, we thought at first of making the ascent ourselves, without a guide, but finally decided to employ a guide. Accordingly, after a lunch we were ready to start.

Our good friend Timmons was a man of stocky build, rather fleshy, and I knew that the climb would be harder for him than for the rest of us, who were also somewhat younger. I cautioned him in regard to starting too rapidly; and so, with alpenstocks in hand, we began with a slow, lazy trudge. The picture shows three of us taking a drink of the cool, clear water from the mountain's melting snows.

For half way up the mountain there was a scanty growth of timber. Beyond the timber-line we came to the snow-fields, where climbing was not quite so easy. The temperature gradually became colder, and the wind stronger. Timmons had to stop and rest at short intervals.

Climbing high mountains goes very hard with some people. As the air becomes rarer, the heart weakens and the body loses strength. One is easily discouraged, and the face takes a serious look, resembling a look of despair. Sometimes bleeding at the nose or ears occurs. I must say I experienced none of these effects on Mount Hood.

We trudged on over snow-fields, moraines, and lava till we arrived at the glacier, where crevasses had to be crossed. One or two dangerous places we passed by the aid of our guide and the lifeline (a rope anchored at the summit and extending down the sides of the mountain for a distance). When Timmons saw the yawning crevasses in the ice, over which we had scrambled partly suspended by the rope, he seriously considered giving up the effort. We did not want him to return home without gaining the summit, so we kept up his courage.

Finally, after pulling ourselves up with the rope, we reached the very top of Mount Hood, 11,225 feet above sea-level. We ascended from the south, and when our vision passed the crest, a wonderful scene was before us on the north. There was the valley of the Columbia, with the river as a silver thread passing through it. Distant from fifty to one hundred fifty miles to the northwest were Mts. Adams, Ranier, and St. Helens, which could be seen to their very bases, and as but a few miles away. Unfortunately, the atmosphere was hazy that day and the vision consequently poor. However, we could distinguish the golden grain-fields of eastern Oregon.

We did not remain long at the summit; for really there was danger of our being blown off and down the steep northern side, and we were cold. The guide, having misjudged the weather a little, had told us we should not need our sweaters or coats. I had on a soft hunting-hat, and in spite of my caution, in an unguarded moment it suddenly left my head and went sailing into the Columbia valley. Soon Timmons met with the same misfortune. Out of kindness to him another hat was loaned him, but it was scarcely on his head till off it went. A handkerchief was then tied on his head, and that too took its departure for unknown regions. Three of us were then hatless. The remaining hat was carefully buttoned up inside its owner's shirt.

The descent was of course more rapid. We slid long distances in the snow, a method which our guide introduced to us, though we had already learned it in the mountains of Canada. We simply sat down in the snow, lifted our feet and away we went, keeping our sitting posture pretty well, but sometimes getting a side twist that resulted in more or less rolling. It was very amusing, but space forbids my giving details.

We reached the Camp about 7:30 P. M., having occupied thirteen hours for the climb. It is needless to say we slept soundly that night. The next morning we accepted some old discarded hats that were offered us. We fished a while in a creek near by, and then started for Portland. We stopped at the residence where we had purchased the cherries and gathered a larger quantity. From this place Timmons telephoned to his home, and in consequence a very appetizing supper awaited our arrival. We related our interesting experiences and felt a sense of satisfaction in being able to say we had climbed Mount Hood.

—*A. L. Byers.*

EDDIE'S RIDE

CHUB was a little bay horse neither pretty nor graceful. His feet were big and clumsy, and sometimes when he trotted, he would get them tangled and fall down. But as he was kind and gentle, Papa bought him for us girls to drive to school. We lived in New Mexico and had to go miles to school. One schoolhouse was five miles west, with not a house between us and it, and the other was six miles east, with only one house on the way. So you see we needed a pony to go such long distances.

Our vehicle was a cart, and when Chub knew we were well tucked in, away he would go. But we had to cross an irrigating ditch, which was sometimes full of water. Chub did hate to get his feet wet; so if we were not careful, he would jump that ditch. You can imagine the jolt we would get.

One of the schoolhouses was near a little river. When we arrived at the schoolhouse, we would stake Chub down by the river-bank to eat the tender grass there while we were busy with our lessons.

Eddie, a boy of ten, was in the habit of loosing the horse every noon and mounting him bareback and bridleless to ride him about. This our father objected to, lest he should let the horse get away and go home. But though we told Eddie our father's objections, he persisted in taking his daily ride, until Chub himself became tired of it.

One day Eddie was on him as usual, digging his bare heels into the horse's ribs and yelling until the poor creature was running round and round. Finally Chub ran straight for the river, right where the quicksand was—in fact, the quicksand was almost everywhere in that river. We all screamed, for we thought that horse and boy would go right in. Eddie lay down on the horse and clung to his neck and mane, calling, "Whoa!" at every breath. Chub ran to the very brink of the river, and, stopping short, whirled around and came back to us girls. Eddie swung clear off the horse, but his hold on Chub's mane kept him out of the water. He picked himself up and walked over to where we were, pale and weak, but a far wiser boy. That was the last time he ever rode Chub.   —*Mabel Hale.*

AN ADVENTURE IN THE WOODS

IT WAS a beautiful sunshiny day in early spring. Birds were singing, brooks were flowing, and all nature seemed to rejoice in being free from cold Winter's grasp.

The children were at home now, school having closed some weeks before. Mama told the boys and girls they might spend the afternoon in the woods. What fun to spend all afternoon gathering wild flowers and roaming among the trees! So the children set out to have a good time. After reaching the woods they found many things to interest childish minds. The girls especially delighted in gathering the bright red berries from the mountain-tea.

"Oh! I found something! Just come and see!" called one of the girls. There in a large hole in a white-oak tree, on a pile of dead leaves lay an opossum. It had been sleeping all winter long and was still drowsy. The girls were afraid to go near, but their brother got a large stick and began hitting the opossum. This did not seem to disturb it much; it just squirmed a little, turned over, and seemed to go to sleep again. After a while the girls ventured near and with their brother, tried to capture the animal. But none of them were very brave.

Finally their brother left them to keep watch while he went home to get Father to come with the gun. The children were anxious to have the opossum killed, for they knew it was an enemy to the neighboring poultry. But Father was busy with his work and said he could not spare the time. What was to be done? Father could not take time to help the children, and they felt it was too great a task for them. Taking courage, the boy returned to the woods where he had left his sisters watching.

"Now, we shall have to kill it ourselves. Father is too busy to come with the gun." "All right, Brother, we'll help you," the girls answered. Then the excitement began. Each child found a large stick for a weapon. You may be sure they all stayed a safe distance from the tree. Finally they succeeded in killing the opossum.

Now for the homeward walk. Four proud children carried their victim home. Mother was much surprized, indeed, to see her children returning with their prize.

These children have grown up to be men and women now, but their minds often go back to the happy, care-free days of their childhood.

—*Rosa Joiner.*

CRIPPLE CREEK

CRIPPLE CREEK, COLO., is located about thirty-five miles from Colorado Springs, nearly ten thousand feet above sea-level, and is one of the highest cities in the United States.

The trip up to this city is undoubtedly one of the grandest and most wonderful in the United States. A great part of the road is carved out of solid rock and makes a very steep and thrilling ride indeed. In many places it does not go around the mountains, but straight up, and in its trip of thirty-five or forty miles it climbs about four thousand feet.

As we traveled along, we could see on one side many other peaks and deep ravines. The color effect was wonderfully beautiful. A look from our window down at the awful abyss below fairly chilled my blood. I thought that should the wheels of our train leave the track we might be hurled down the seemingly bottomless depths to our death. It was a time of the year, too, when there were numerous washouts caused by the heavy rains, and traveling was somewhat dangerous. We passed many narrow places and through rough, rocky walls, and thus after a

thrilling but very enjoyable ride we came to Altman, which is said to be the highest incorporated town in the world. Here we stopped but a short time, and after passing other rich and important gold-mining camps we reached our destination, Cripple Creek, the heart of one of the richest gold-mining camps in the world.

The city is situated on a group of hills. One can hardly travel in any direction there without climbing a hill. Nearly all these hills are drilled by some prospector in search for gold. Some prospectors have found great wealth there, while others only poverty, spending much money in prospecting and planning to find gold, but getting none. Though untold millions were hidden in the hills in this region, yet many people there were nearly starving for lack of money to buy bread. Some of them thought they had rich claims, but said it might take time to eventually work to the rich vein of gold; so they thus toiled on day after day, often receiving nothing whatever for their toil except when they might happen upon a little valuable ore. The condition of the poor here is sad, because some of them are too fascinated in their search for gold even to provide for their families as they should. Those who are able continue the search and with improved machinery often strike rich claims and become wealthy.

The gold in this region is all found underground, and usually runs in veins in the hard rock. This is hewn out, the rock crushed and then placed in extreme heat, where all the dross is removed, then the precious metal is molded into bulk and shipped away. Cripple Creek gold is known nearly everywhere, and many people wear it upon their persons, in their teeth, and in many other ways. It is mostly used for beauty or durability.   —*H. C. Hawkins.*

DEER-HUNTING IN OREGON

IT IS a treat for one who has always lived in the East to take a hunting trip in the Rogue River Mountains of southwestern Oregon, where, in sections remote from man's habitation, one realizes he is indeed in Nature's wild. The open season for deer having arrived, we secured our hunting-licenses and provided supplies and cooking-utensils. We left Grant's Pass on the morning of July 31, and proceeded some twenty miles by wagon. There were eight of us in number, besides a boy. There were three teams, including a team of burrows and colt belonging to Joe Hill. This man, a prospector and hunter, was acquainted with the country and the trails, and we chose him as our guide.

We camped for dinner at Merlin, and in the afternoon passed some beautiful scenery on Rogue River. The road in some places hugged close to the mountain, while on the lower side was a frightful precipice descending from the very wheels of the wagon. We crossed the river on an old-fashioned ferry that was propelled by the current, and camped for the night at Taylor Creek. We had already seen some deer-tracks.

We slept out-of-doors with the beautiful canopy of heaven above us. There was no rain at that time of year, and shelter was unnecessary. Sleeping out-of-doors was new to me, but I soon became used to it and slept soundly. We would soften our beds by laying fir-boughs under our blankets.

On the second day, after traveling as far as we could by wagon, we arranged our pack-train of horses and burrows, and prepared for about thirty miles of trail. Bear Camp was our destination, which we reached on the evening of August 2.

I walked nearly the whole of this distance. The trail would lead up and down the mountain, or along the crest, or on top of a ridge, or through dense forests, around trees and fallen timber, forming the most twisty path one can imagine. The little burrow colt became very tired, and Hill said that once on going up a steep grade near the end of our journey the intelligent little thing took hold of its mother's tail so as to be helped up the hill. The mother promptly kicked it loose, as she had her own load to carry.

In the afternoon of our first day on the trail we camped early. Hill  decided he would take a hunt for deer yet that evening, and invited me to go with him. We left the trail and canvassed a mountain-slope. As we were about to return I suggested that we roll some stones down the slope and scare out the deer if there were any. He said it would be a good idea. Just then he spied the head of a buck deer projecting from the bushes some distance below us. The animal was lying down. Hill called to me to be still and then fired, but missed. I took the second shot and missed. It is a common thing to aim too high when shooting down a decline. By this time we saw there were two deer, but both disappeared. Soon we saw them again away across the ravine going up the opposite slope. As we had long-range rifles, we fired again, but our bullets only kicked up the dust about them. The creatures were confused, not knowing which way to turn, as they could not see us. Soon they disappeared again.

Thus I had my first shot at a deer. My next shot at one, a day or two after we reached Bear Camp, was successful, and the animal fell, shot through the back. Another deer had been killed that same morning by one of our party, and so we had venison from that on.

After a few days at Bear Camp, several members of our party returned home, while the remainder of us went five miles farther to Bobb's Garden. Here we found a deserted cabin which we used. This was higher up in the mountains and in a heavy forest. After learning the trails about this place, I arose one morning before daylight and started out for deer. I wanted to be where the deer were by daybreak. While moving cautiously along, I saw a deer a few rods below me standing still and gazing at me. The law forbade the killing of does, and wanting to be sure this one was a buck, I hesitated until I could discern between the branches of his horns and the branches of the trees. By the time I

was ready to fire, I felt the "buck fever" creeping over me, and discovered I was so nervous that I could not take steady aim. The result was a shameful miss. By the time I could fire again the buck had disappeared. One feels chagrined over such failures, but they belong to one's first experience in hunting. When I shot the deer I killed a few days before, I never thought of nervousness.

I was anxious to kill a bear or a cougar (mountain-lion). These animals were plentiful enough, but were harder to find than the deer. One of our party fired at a bear, but probably shot too high, and the bear lost no time in getting away. One day I canvassed a dismal canyon in the hope of finding a bear, but was disappointed. It is estimated that a cougar in that country kills, on an average, one deer every two weeks, or twenty-six in a year.

Space will forbid my relating more of the details of our hunting-trip. It was not the hunting alone that interested me. Of all the experiences in my Western tour, this one in the mountains of Oregon was the most dear to me. There was not the rugged beauty of the Canadian Rockies. There was not the melting snows, the dashing streams, the sublime heights; but there was a charm I can not express that belongs to these hunting-grounds in mid-summer, these mountain-slopes where grow the manzanita, the mountain-laurel, the thimbleberries, the huckleberries of blue, red, and white varieties, and various other kinds of vegetation. Nature abounds in her loveliness under the August skies.

At times while out all alone I would sit on some sunny ledge and give place to meditation and prayer. I would think of the dear ones many hundreds of miles away. It is at these times that a person recalls his failures. He feels so little among these mighty things and beautiful things of nature, and thinks of how he might be a better person in life. Sometimes I would feel a tinge of loneliness, or homesickness, and my emotions would take the form of tears.

Soon our short span of life will have reached its full; these mountains and rocks and monarchs of the woods will continue just as they are, but we shall have passed away. "Oh why should the spirit of mortal be proud!" These reveries help us to see ourselves just as we are. I love these mountains and forests and canyons, and it is principally on their account that this deer-hunting expedition shall always have a place in my memory.

There is another thing I almost forgot, and must mention. We returned to Bear Camp, and after staying all night there started early in the morning for home. On gaining the crest of the first ridge, we were greeted by a wonderful sight. The clouds had dropped during the night, and there they were as a vast ocean below us. As far as the eye could reach, and for about two thirds of the compass, there was a sea of clouds, their roughness appearing as rolling waves and the mountain-tops as islands. We had to pass down through these clouds, and as we were doing so, our clothing became soaked. I had never seen such a sight before, and it may never again be my privilege to behold such a wonder.

—*A. L. Byers.*

THREE GIRLS BLACKBERRYING

ONE summer afternoon three young girls went blackberrying. Their mama was glad to let them go and have a good time, but told them to come back early. Their brother hitched the horse to the carriage, and they climbed in, taking pails and baskets, and soon were off. They intended going about a mile and a half from home and were to return before time for supper.

When they arrived at the place where they had planned to stop, they found that several other people had come there for berries, and that it would not pay to stop, as there would not be berries enough for all.

The eldest girl told her sisters that they would drive on about two miles farther to their father's woodland farm, which was used as a pasture for sheep. There the blackberry-bushes grew in abundance, and they could pick all the berries they wanted. The younger girls agreed that this would be the best thing that they could do; so they drove on.

It was about half-past two when they arrived at the woodland. Hitching their horse, they started across the swamp which lay between them and the blackberry-patch. Soon they were in the midst of the berry-bushes higher than their heads and loaded with ripe, juicy berries. The berries were so large and the small pails that the girls carried filled up so quickly that they determined to fill the half-bushel basket they had brought with them. They talked of how pleased their dear mama would be, and they worked with a will.

But it was late when they began picking, and before they were aware of it, the six-o'clock whistle blew and dusk was settling down upon the earth. Having finished filling the basket, they started back across the swamp. They were in such a hurry that they did not stop to find the path, but went running through the bushes, splashing through mud and water, and caring little where they stepped. The sun had set, and they were unable to tell in which direction to go; but they could hear the neighing of the horse and the bleating of the sheep on the other side of the swamp. By going in the direction from which these sounds came, they got safely across. They knew the road well from here and started home feeling well satisfied with their afternoon's work.

The moon was shining brightly, and the ride was so enjoyable and refreshing after the hurried trip through the swamp that they drove along slowly, now and then singing snatches of some song, and little thinking of the anxiety they were causing their parents.

When within about a mile of home, they met their papa, who had started out to find them. Their mama had thought that perhaps the horse had run away with them or something else dreadful had happened, as they should have been home long before this time. She was so nervous and frightened that she had their papa to go in search of them. The girls' papa told them to drive to the home of their grandparents and let them know that they were safe while he hurried home and set the mother's mind at rest.

When the girls reached home, their mother was very glad to see them, but looked so pale and worn that they were very sorry they had been so thoughtless and had caused her so much anxiety. They told her they had thought only of pleasing her with the berries and had not realized that the time was passing so rapidly.

Their papa then told them that the swamp which they had crossed was several miles long and that if they had gone in the wrong direction or had not heard the horse and sheep they might have gone a long time without coming to any road and might have been lost days before any one would have found them. The girls were very thankful that God had watched over them and helped them to reach home safely, and decided to be more thoughtful in the future.

Many times girls and boys do things carelessly and thoughtlessly, giving no heed to what the consequences may be and thus cause their parents needless anxiety and suffering. Worry causes persons to grow old very quickly; I am sure that none of my readers would like to think that their thoughtlessness had caused their parents to have gray hair and care-worn faces before they otherwise would. Let us be as thoughtful in every way as we can and be careful not to give our parents trouble.

—*Eva Johnson Grice.*

TO MOUNT SHASTA'S SUMMIT

MOUNT SHASTA, in northern California, is rather more famous than Mount Hood, as it rises over three thousand feet higher into the sky. It is only a few miles from Sisson, the nearest railway station on the Southern Pacific.

It is interesting to watch for Shasta when approaching it from the north on the railroad. Standing high above the other mountains, its snowy top presents a beautiful sight. But one sees it first on one side of the train then on the other, as if it were playing hide and seek. This is because the railroad is so winding.

Starting on foot in company with two friends, I left Sisson in the evening at seven o'clock, intending to make the summit of Shasta and return, a distance of twenty-four miles, in a night and a day. We were equipped with only a lantern and a light lunch. Once we lost our trail, but found it again after considerable searching. We proceeded until we began to feel tired. Building a small fire, we tried to sleep on the

bare earth, but found we could get no restful sleep; so on we went, reaching the timberline at day break. After stopping to eat the lunch we had brought with us, we started for the summit.

Shasta is not really difficult to climb and not so dangerous as Hood. One of our party had been up before, and we did not employ a regular guide. But Shasta served me as many are served when climbing high mountains. After leaving the timber-line, I began to feel a slight sickness, and became weak and would stagger. I found it difficult to breathe, and the higher we ascended the worse these feelings became.

Weakened in body, I was also weakened in every other way. I had heard of people going insane on Mount Shasta, and wandering around, not knowing where they were. I began to feel uneasy, and was tormented with the thought that perhaps I should share the same fate. The men who were with me had blackened their faces in order to prevent severe sunburn. Whenever I looked at them, they reminded me of the devil, and, foolish as it may seem, this thought troubled me. They got pretty far ahead of me, and this too discouraged me. I learned how to sympathize with people who are weak bodily, mentally, and spiritually. I could not understand why I was having this trouble; for on Mount Hood I had felt very vigorous, and that, too, after losing sleep the night before. There was, however, this disadvantage with the Shasta trip: I had walked nearly all night, and had started for the summit that morning with my nerves somewhat taxed. Then, too, this mountain being in a warmer latitude, its atmosphere was less invigorating.

But I had no thought of turning back, and was determined to reach the top. I stopped to rest near Thumb Rock, at a sunny spot, sheltered from the wind. But I found it was better for me in the cool breeze, so started on again. Above me was nearly a half mile of loose lava, which gave no firm foothold. But here the thought of being so near the top encouraged me. I simply persisted until I reached the very summit, and then lay down exhausted. Never before had I felt so nearly dead. We were 14,440 feet, nearly three miles, above the sea.

Shasta, like Hood, was once an active volcano. After the first cone was formed by the lava piling up, an eruption burst out at the side, forming a new crater. Thus, Shasta, when seen from certain directions, shows a double cone. The newer and lower crater is called Shastina. One can look over into the crater from the summit of the main peak.

We reached the summit of the mountain at two o'clock, and remained long enough to look around a little and leave our names in a registry which we found there. I was not interested in anything just then, and do not remember what we did see from the summit.

On beginning to descend, I immediately felt stronger. We slid in the snow for some distance, as we had done on Mount Hood. We reached the timber-line at four o'clock, and after lunching, took the trail for home, arriving at eight in the evening, exceedingly tired.

I must not omit a mention of Shasta Springs, situated a few miles below Sisson. Here all passenger-trains stop, in order that the passengers may get a drink of Shasta water as it bubbles out of the earth. This is a natural soda-water, containing a large percentage of iron and magnesia, highly charged with carbonic acid gas. When flavored with lemon or other flavor, and sweetened, it is a close imitation of what may be purchased at the soda-fountains.

These springs are in a beautiful glen where streams, born of Shasta snows, come tumbling over the high cliffs in numerous waterfalls. Moss and ferns and cascades are abundant, and it is a delightful spot to visit.

—*A. L. Byers.*

A NOBLE BOY

THIRTY years ago, in the forests of northern Pennsylvania, lived a family of honest, industrious people. The father earned a living by his sawmill. The oldest child, a boy of seventeen, named George, was a great help to his father. One day the forest-fires swept down the mountain-side and reduced the mill to a mass of charred ruins. George saw at once that there were too many to be fed unless work was obtained.

He decided to leave home, seek employment, and send his savings to his dear mother. She gave him a pocket-knife, a Bible, and her blessing, and sent him out on an October day to find a place in the busy world. George was a brave boy. He found it hard to say farewell to his parents and his sisters and brothers, but he had decided. Duty called him. His good mother could scarcely keep back the tears as she kissed him and said, "My son, be honest and trust in the Lord."

Two weeks passed by. George could not find work. Late one evening, in a cold rain, he was climbing the Allegheny Mountains near Galitzin, on his way to Johnstown. At the latter place he thought he could find employment in the large iron factories. He had slept the night before in a barn. He had eaten nothing all day, and he had not one cent in his pocket.

In the twilight he saw a boy coming from a miner's cabin. George asked the boy, "Will you please tell me where I can spend the night?"

"There is a farmer just above, who might keep you," said the boy, "but he is not as kind to travelers as he might be."

George thanked the boy, and hurried on to the farmhouse. He

knocked at the door and was met by the farmer, to whom he said, "Will you please allow me to sleep in your barn? I am tired and my clothes are wet. Besides, I am a stranger in these parts."

"No," growled the farmer, "I don't keep tramps. They carry matches and may burn my barn."

"Sir, I never carry matches; I will promise you to be careful and to leave at daybreak. Please allow me to sleep in the barn," pleaded George.

But the farmer was hard-hearted, and George plodded on in the rain and in the darkness. At last he came to a place where two roads branched. Which should he take? He paused a moment, and then, falling upon his knees, he asked the Lord to guide him. When he arose he took the road to the right, and late that night reached Galitzin.

The poor boy was too tired to think. He walked into a hotel and asked the landlord to give him a bed. This the landlord did, and George slept soundly till morning. Then he wondered how he could pay for his lodging. He went downstairs and said to the landlord: "I was so tired last evening that I did not tell you I had no money for fear you would turn me away. Here is my pocket-knife; please take it and keep it until I send you the money for my lodging; then send it to me, as it is a present from my mother."

"But you have had no breakfast," said the landlord, his heart touched by the young man's story. "Go into the dining-room, eat all you want, keep your knife, and pay me when you can."

George was too grateful to speak. He walked into the dining-room and sat down to a warm meal. There were roast potatoes, ham, and eggs, and hot rolls. How he did eat! It seemed that he had never before enjoyed such a feast. Then he thanked the man who had so kindly cared for him, and set out for Ebensburg, on his way to Johnstown.

On the road to Ebensburg, George sat down to read from his Bible. He was comforted by reading, "Yet have I not seen the righteous forsaken, nor his seed begging bread."

On the way his shoes, soaked by the mud and rain, showed opened seams and loose soles. He feared that he would soon be barefoot. Just then he spied a long wax-end in the road. With this he repaired his shoes and plodded on.

Late in the afternoon he arrived at Ebensburg. He walked into the post-office and said, "If you will trust me for a postal card, I will pay you for it as soon as I can.'' He was given the postal card. He wrote to his mother, telling her he was well, and was pushing along to a place in which he thought he could get work.

George noticed a stout man standing by him in the post-office, but did not speak to him. Penniless and hungry the boy started for Johnstown. As he passed down the road, he noticed the stout man following him. Too sad to enjoy company, George walked faster; so did the stout man. Finally, George heard a call, ''Young man, please wait a bit.'' George obeyed. The man came up and in a kind voice asked where he was going.

''To Johnstown, sir; I believe I am on the right road.''

''You are,'' was the answer, ''but where will you spend the night?''

''I hope to find a farmer down the road who will allow me to sleep in his barn.''

''My friend, it is miles to the nearest place of shelter. Won't you come back to Ebensburg, spend the night with me, and start afresh in the morning?''

George believed that the Lord had sent this man, who was a Swedish missionary, to care for him. They walked back together. George told his story to the man and went to bed.

To his great delight, the next morning the man gave him a ticket to Johnstown and sent him to friends in the latter place, who helped him to obtain work. George paid back every cent given him on his journey.

A few years ago George went to Ebensburg again. In the hotel one night he told me this story. He is now a talented man, and his goodness is known far and wide.   —*G. J. Galentine.*

FIGHTING A RATEL

IN AFRICA there flourishes a curious, long-nosed little creature called the ratel, which is said to exhibit a most peculiar method in fighting its human adversaries. The son of a Britisher in South Africa, who was using a shotgun for the first time, had an exciting time with a ratel.

The boy saw the ratel creeping around an ant-hill. It cantered off at a not very lively pace, and the boy fired at easy range. The animal turned heels-over-head, much in the same way that a tame squirrel will disport himself in a wheel-cage. The ratel paused once, as if in pain, but never took his eyes off the boy. The lad did not think of running away, but clubbed his gun and stood facing the animal, prepared to meet a spring.

It happened that this English boy had never been told how the ratel fights. Almost every boy in the veldt knows, but this lad did not. To wait thus, expecting a leap breast high, is to give the ratel exactly the chance he wants. Hesitating a second, the ratel glided swiftly in and seized the boy's feet. The boy hacked him with the butt of his gun, kicked at him, shouted his loudest, but the ratel gnawed away with the pertinacity of a bull-dog. At every blow, the creature's teeth closed like a vise. The boy seized its long tail, wrenched and twisted it, but the ratel would not drop his hold.

The struggle lasted for a shorter time than it takes to tell it. The muscles of the lad's instep were cut through, and he tumbled backward, not at full length, but against an ant-hill. This circumstance probably saved his life.

The ratel let go, as it does when its victim drops, to spring upon the body. But the plucky boy lifted himself upon his elbows and lay across the summit of the mound. That might only have prolonged the struggle, but at that moment his father came running up. The boy was many months in bed and many more on crutches.   —*Selected.*

SHIPWRECKED AT SEA

THE sea was calm when the large vessel with its immense white wings sailed out upon the broad ocean. A large number of passengers were on board and also a valuable cargo, which was to be taken far down the coast of one of the countries of Europe. When sailing was good and the weather favorable, the vessel took far enough to sea to lose sight of the rocky cliffs.

Harold and Margaret, aged about fourteen and sixteen, respectively, were accompanying their aunt upon this particular voyage and were greatly enjoying the merry chase the waves were giving each other upon the ocean's broad expanse. Some birds flew here and there, and occasionally bits of wood were seen floating upon the surface—presumably from some wreck.

Far away and close to the horizon were seen threatening clouds, which continued gathering thicker and growing blacker until a fearful storm and almost night-like blackness surrounded the vessel. The sail-

ors were hurrying here and there, working to clear the decks before the storm.

"Why are the people so frightened?" spoke Margaret, "and why do they run here and there in such a manner?"

"I do not know," responded Harold, "unless they are afraid the storm will wreck the ship."

"But why should they be so frightened?"

"Maybe an awful storm is coming," answered the boy again. "Let us go back to the stateroom and pray. I know that is what mother would do if she were here and felt that danger was near."

Hand in hand the two went back into their room and knelt down beside the bed, and with their youthful faces turned upward they prayed their simple prayers for protection.

The awful storm had gathered and the terrific wind was tearing the sails and breaking the masts. The ship also tossed about and became unmanageable. Though it was only a few miles from the mainland, yet there was great danger of its being wrecked upon the rocks and those on board lost.

The sailors knew very well the grave danger they were in; for the rocky coast had also many half-hidden rocks far out in the sea, upon which the vessel might be wrecked.

Closer and closer the ship was driven toward the rocky coast, despite all the sailors could do. The officers ordered the life-boats prepared while life-belts were being distributed among the passengers, who were all on deck with the exception of the little Christians, who, despite the tossings of the boat, continued in prayer for their deliverance.

There was great excitement among the passengers on deck when a crash was heard.

"We're on the rocks;" exclaimed one of the officers, "and the ship's going down! To the life-boats!"

No time was lost in obeying his command, and one boat after another was fast being filled.

The lady in whose care the two youths were placed thought that Margaret and Harold were among the crowd until after many of the passengers were in the life-boats. Excitedly she looked about and exclaimed, "Where are the children?" No one seemed to know anything about them. The captain accompanied the lady in search of them and hurried to the room.

The door stood ajar, and when they peeped in, both were struck with awe at the scene. There the children were kneeling and, with faces upturned and eyes closed, were calm and unconscious of any danger. Margaret was just saying, "Lord, do not let any harm come to us, but bring us back safe to Mama."

Knowing that the situation was grave and that no time was to be lost, the aunt and the captain hurried the children to the boats. Although the risk was great, yet the life-boats finally reached shore and every passenger was saved.

Throughout the whole affair Harold and Margaret were the least excited of all the crowd, and when all were safely landed, Margaret said, "We might have all been lost if we had not prayed the Lord to save and protect us."   —Wm. A. Bixler.

THE HEROIC DEED OF GRACE DARLING

BECAUSE a person is always "in the lead" and assuming brave attitudes, we can not decide that he is a hero. The heroes of the past have been those people who, during some trying scene when every nerve was strained, rose to the occasion and, regardless of self, without premeditation, did naturally the deed that relieved the situation. There is an element in the character of the hero that forgets self to serve others. There are many heroes that have never been mentioned in history. The brave, enduring toilers of every-day life around us are heroes; unselfishly they sacrifice the best that comes to them, in the service of others. At the expense of self, they rescue many lives.

Many years ago a girl who lived on the Farne Islands, in the middle of the sea, showed true heroism. She knew the sea, and perhaps little else. She could manage the oar, and well understood the mad ragings of the ocean and its dangers. Her duty was to send the light out over the ocean, so that ships might steer clear of the rocks and escape the perils of the waters.

One night there came a terrible storm on the sea. The waves rose like mountains and dashed with terrific force. Neither the girl nor her parents could sleep that night as they thought of the perils at sea.

On this same night, Sept. 6, 1838, a steamer on her way from Hull to Dundee reached the open sea off Spurnhead. A poor ship to begin with, she soon began to feel the strain of the dashing waves. Her boilers leaked and were strained and torn until the ship could not be managed. It was split in two and forty persons perished as the stern of the vessel went down. Near this point were rocks that extended down into the sea one hundred fathoms. On these the wind hurled the bow of the vessel with nine passengers and sailors. Here they were swept by the waves and buffeted by the storm while they waited for the dawn and prayed for help.

At dawn Grace Darling, searching the sea with her telescope, discovered them, and determined at once to help them. Her mother pleaded with her child not to face the danger, but the girl could not stay. She said, "If father will not go with me, I will go alone." Her mother then helped her to launch the boat, and Grace Darling and her brave father, undaunted by danger, battled with the winds and angry waters until they rescued the perishing strangers.

In a few days the world knew of this heroic deed and money and presents were lavished upon her. Her fame was world-wide, and her name in history represents one of the bravest girls that ever lived.

Self-denial and sacrifice will rescue many souls today, but recompense and fame must not be the object. As Grace Darling risked her life for nine, may we by self-abnegation and well-doing lead others to know that a life has been sacrificed that all might live.

—*Mabel C. Porter.*

UP PIKE'S PEAK

THE elevation of Pike's Peak is 14,147 feet above sea-level. It is not the highest peak in Colorado. There are upwards of twenty peaks higher than it, though none of them exceed it more than about three hundred feet.

The first part of the trip was pleasant enough. We did not need to worry about the trail, for the railroad marked our course, and we knew that where it went we could go. The railroad winds considerably, and the scenery is interesting enough; but when we got up pretty high into the rarefied air we found it a little difficult to breathe and of course had to go slowly, and with as little exertion as possible. The man who was with me became rather short of breath and had to rest frequently.

By the time we reached the summit, darkness was fast approaching and a fierce blizzard was raging. All thoughts of returning that same evening were abandoned, and we were compelled to remain all night on the summit of Pike's Peak. The novelty of it suited me pretty well, even if it was a matter of a little endurance.

Frozen to death on Pike's Peak Aug 21, 1911

There is a house and an observatory on the summit, at the end of the cog railroad. The accommodations were somewhat crude, but we did not mind that. The rarefied condition of the air affected us a little, and I could notice the difference in the action of my heart. On going to bed I was a little fearful that if I should lie down my heart might stop. I trusted all with the Lord, however, and went to sleep. I awoke a time or two during the night, but by morning felt that I had had a pretty fair night's rest.

By morning the temperature had dropped to within seven degrees of the zero point and considerable snow had fallen. It seemed cold for the middle of October. I paid five cents for a glass of water. Water had to be conveyed there and of course it could not be had free. It seemed odd to have to buy water.

When we started down the mountain, we had snow to wade, and as we had not brought our overcoats we became a little cold. However, as we went on and farther and farther down, breathing became easier and we grew warmer. After passing Windy Point we were in the shelter of the mountain for the rest of the way.

Now I must tell you something sad that happened on Pike's Peak in the month of August, about two months before we made our climb. A man and wife from Texas were frozen to death when within half a mile of the sunmmit. Being from Texas, they perhaps did not understand the northern cold, as they were but thinly dressed, having no underwear nor extra clothing.

But they were very unwise in not heeding the advice that others gave them. A storm was on, and they were warned not to attempt climbing to the summit that day, especially as they were thinly dressed. The woman had only a thin summer waist, but finally accepted a shawl which she was urged to take. Her husband would have turned back. but she persisted. The conductor on the evening trip down warned them not to go farther and offered to carry them back free, but still the woman persisted. She was going up Pike's Peak whether or no. She said, "You can't freeze a Texan."

As the conductor was then on the last trip down that day, there was no further chance for them to return. It was learned by telephone late that evening that they had not reached the summit-house, and so people knew what their fate had been. In the morning they were found beside the railroad lying just as shown in the picture—the result of not heeding faithful advice.   —*A. L. Byers.*

AN INDIAN CHIEF'S GRAVE

THE sun rose large, beautiful, and clear from behind the horizon, and shed its mellow rays across the broad expanse of level prairie. It was one of those mornings when the air is so clear and exhilarating that every breath can be felt at the bottom of one's lungs. It was spring. The birds were singing gaily, especially the sweet-voiced meadow-lark; the sky was clear and calm; the grass was a tender green, and the young grain was just up, making the fields look like great carpets covering hundreds of acres. Such was the morning when we decided to start on our twelve- or fifteen-mile drive to visit the Indian chief's grave, on the south bank of Eagle Creek in Western Canada.

After eating breakfast and preparing our lunch, we climbed into the buggies and started. We much enjoyed the delightful air as we rode along. There were six in our company—five grown persons and one small child.

After driving for about two hours across the level prairie, we arrived at the north bank of Eagle Creek. Here it seemed we were on high ground, but in reality the creek was very low. From this side we had a good view of the other side, which we intended reaching, but we had to go a long, roundabout way to get there. We could see the lovely bright green on the other side, and it appeared to be grass covering the sides of the range of hills along the creek. We drove a mile or so farther west and came to a small village, where we bought some oranges and a few other things to add to our lunch. Then we turned somewhat south, and began winding our way up the hills, not knowing how we should manage to get to the top with the horses and buggies. But after going some distance we found a well-graded road that lead to the very top. We climbed one range of hills, then reached a large level portion of

country. On this level ground were some attractive farms. Then came the climb of the last hills, which were by far the steepest. I felt sorry for the horses. Some of the company got off and walked, as they wished to ease the horses. Finally, after winding in and out and resting several times, we reached the top, and again were on quite level ground.

Hurrying eastward as fast as possible, we came upon a small house, where we inquired if we were near the chief's grave. We thought we saw it a short distance ahead, but wished to make sure, so as not to have to drive out of the way. Learning that we were right, we hastened on. Soon we were on the spot. Then, after unhitching the horses and feeding them, we turned to investigate all there was to be seen about the place.

As far as can be learned, nobody knows the name of the chief who is buried here. As seen in the picture, there was a large heap of stones; but some one has dug up his body, and now there are wild gooseberry-stalks growing among the stones. It remains unknown who committed the deed, for there is a heavy penalty resting upon such work. When the Government received this country from the Indian tribes that then roamed over it, it signed a treaty with the Indians that none of their chiefs' graves should ever be touched; therefore there is a large reward offered to any one who can give any trace of the person or persons who removed the chief's body.

As I said before, there is a large heap of stones, and these are arranged in a circle, perhaps about ten feet across. From this center there are rows of stones leading east, southeast, south, southwest, and west. At the end of each row are other graves. These graves are supposed to be those of his family. The rows have stones ranging from eighteen to thirty-five in number. We concluded that the number of stones in each row indicated the number of summers each Indian had lived; for Indians counted their years by the summers they lived.

From this point we had a grand view of the surrounding country. To the north of us was the valley in whose lowest bed ran Eagle Creek, with large ravines running up to the high plain on which we now were. From the bed of the creek to the height where the grave lies there is an elevation of more than seven hundred feet.

You remember that I mentioned seeing, when we were on the other side, what appeared to be grass making the sides of the hills look green? In reality what we saw were large ravines filled with poplar-trees. Now we could look down on these and plainly see that they were trees. With the naked eye we could see towns fifty miles to the east of us and nearly the same distance south, but only about thirty-five miles west, as some hills closed off the view in that direction. To the north we could see villages and lakes within a range of at least twenty-five miles. Taking our excellent field-glasses, which we had not forgotten to bring with us, we could see things much more plainly.

Having satisfied ourselves that we had seen all there was to be seen, we went down the slope of one of the ravines, and upon finding a suitable place, spread our lunch on the grass and sat down to eat. After lunch a few of us went farther down among the trees, gathered some wild flowers, and broke branches of green leaves off the trees. These we took home, for one does not see many trees on the level prairies.

Becoming satisfied with our ramble over valleys, hills, and rocks. and with our sight-seeing, we hitched the horses, climbed into the buggies, and commenced our homeward journey. We took an altogether different route from what we took coming. There was still a considerable stretch of hills and valleys to cross, and while some of the party were going out of the way with the buggies, some of us walked and "cut corners." This we enjoyed, as the old grass had been burned in the early spring, and the new was lovely and green After awhile we took the rigs, and, going some distance farther, we again crossed Eagle

Creek. As there were stones piled in it for a bridge, we dismounted, and by careful stepping, got across without getting wet feet. After climbing a few more steep hills, gathering a few wild cactus as we went, we finally reached level prairie again. We went across several plowed fields, which were not at all smooth riding, before we came to a good trail (roads there were called trails).

It was rather late when we reached home, and after having a good supper, we retired as soon as possible, and slept soundly.

—*Lucy R. Hines.*

CROSSING THE ATLANTIC

The Start

I HAD made all plans to sail on the Lusitania when the news came that she had been sunk by a submarine. I found, however, that there was an American vessel, called the New York, scheduled to sail on May 25, 1915, from Liverpool, England.

I hastened to Liverpool, only to find that all first- and second-class accommodations had been taken, and that my only choice was to go third-class. Feeling that it was the Lord's will for me to come to America at this time, I booked for third-class passage.

Two o'clock, May 25, found me amongst a crowd of third-class passengers lined up on the wharf. Here we were questioned as to our nationality, destination, etc. A doctor, by means of a small, bright instrument, turned up our eyelids to see if we were infected with any dangerous disease. It is said that disease can be detected under the eyelids before it is noticeable anywhere else.

Amongst the crowd I noticed a superior-looking young man, and I determined to become acquainted with him. I spoke to him on the wharf, and we passed up the gangway together. Then we passed along the side of the ship, around the stern, and back on the other side to the forepart of the ship. We were told our sleeping-places were "for'd."

When we arrived at the forepart of the vessel, we descended a stairway to our sleeping apartment. How surprised we were! That part of the ship was divided off into partitions, or boxes. These boxes were about eight feet square, and each contained four shelves. In each shelf there were a dirty mattress, a pillow, and a sort of bedcover. Two of these shelves were to be occupied by my friend and me; the other two were occupied by two other men.

The steward down there must have noticed the disgusted look on our faces. He said, "You'll be all right here, boys." But we had serious doubts about it. We left our hand-baggage in there and went up on deck. I asked my new-found friend where he had come from. "From South Africa," he replied. He was going to America. And soon I found that he was a genuine Christian; so I felt very glad at the thought of having his company during the voyage.

The ship waited at the dock till night; then the ropes were pulled away, and a tug pulled and strained at the vessel till she was out towards the river Mersey. Here we lay till late in the evening, then the ship's engines began moving.

About 11 P. M. we went down to our bunks. Sleep was impossible. The crew overhead made a most fearful noise. Evidently they were cleaning up the vessel. The stuffiness and disagreeableness became so unbearable that at 4 A. M. I got up and went on deck. We were now out in the Irish Sea, fairly on our way; but a fog prevailed, and we could not see anything.

Out on the Ocean

After breakfast the next morning my friend and I decided to go up on the top deck and look around. Alas! the top deck was reserved for first- and second-class passengers, and we could not go on it. We had to be content with the second deck

As night came on we thought about our having to sleep in our bunks; but our thoughts were not at all pleasant. Later on, however, we went down. My friend went to bed; but the smell of the place was such that I could not endure it, so I ran up on deck again. I lay down on a deck-seat and tried to sleep. There I had at least plenty of fresh air. Soon my friend came up from below fully dressed. He said he could not endure it any longer down there. Then a young Italian and a Swiss came up, and we all slept the best we could on the benches.

The third night the sea began to grow rough, and we began to feel sick. Seasickness is a very trying form of sickness. A person feels that he does not care what else happens if only he can get rid of that feeling in his stomach. My friend and I looked around and found a dry passageway. Then from our bunks we brought up the pillows and bedcovers. These, with our overcoats made a pretty fair bed, and we had a good sleep that night. But the next night the sea became so wild that it beat in and before we knew it wet our bedclothes. We rose and dragged our bedding to a place a little higher. We tried to sleep again; but we were soon aroused by the gruff voice of a sailor who said, "You'd better clear out of this if you don't want to get wet." As it was near morning anyway, we took his advice.

That day a brilliant idea came to our minds. There was a table in one corner of our dining-room not far from where the cooking was done. No one ever ate at this table, and we thought that we could put our bedding under there and have that for our sleeping-place for the remainder of the voyage. The thought of our having to go back to our bunks was intolerable, as the awful smell grew worse there every day.

We spoke to the steward about our sleeping under the table; but he said it was against the rules of the ship. We were determined, however, and talked till he stopped to argue. We took his arguing for consent; then we fixed our bedding under the table. It was fine there. We had plenty of fresh air, and heat from the cooking-place. Here we slept comfortably though the storm did increase.

While the storm raged, the ocean presented a sight we shall never forget. As far as the eye could see, there was one mass of heaving, tossing waters, breaking into foam and dashing their spray into the air. The good ship tossed, and plunged into the oncoming waves till they broke right over her top deck. But none could sink her. Above the greatest she, like some living thing, rose triumphant and bore us safely on to the city of New York, which place we reached ten days after we left Liverpool.

Getting into New York

We passed the Statue of Liberty early in the morning. Soon we anchored at the quay, but we were not yet free to go off board. First- and second-class passengers were allowed to leave the ship, have their luggage examined, and go to their respective destinations; but all third-class passengers had to go to Ellis Island for examination.

Our luggage was examined by a colored official, who was very polite. We were then put on a ferry, and after many delays we finally started for Ellis Island. When we arrived there, we began to undergo government inspection. First we were arranged in a circle in a big hall, then an official told us to take off our hats. I do not know for what purpose he made this request. It was an inconvenience to the women to take off their hats and carry them, as their hands were full of luggage. We passed through a long hall, at the end of which stood a tall official who looked each of us over carefully before he let us pass.

Next we came to a man who had in his hand one of the same sort of bright, little instruments the doctor at Liverpool had. He also turned our eyelids inside out, but he was very kind and did it as gently as he could.

Having passed this last official, the men were sent to one apartment and the women to another to undress, so that we could be more thoroughly examined. This examination, including undressing and dressing again, required some time. When it was over, we were marched into a long hall full of benches, where we were told to sit down. At the farther end of the hall were counters, behind which were some officials. We waited a long time. Some of our number were brought before the officials and afterwards allowed to pass out; but a bell rang before all were dealt with, and the officials went to dinner, leaving the remaining ones of us to wait.

They came back in about an hour; and then we were again called up in turn and asked where we were going and how much money we had. We had to show the money. Finally we got through, resolved that we would never again, if we could possibly avoid it, cross the ocean third-class.

Regretfully I said good-by to my friend and made my way to a missionary home. Here I was well received, and soon recovered from the effects of the voyage.   —*James Turner*.

DOWN INTO A COAL MINE

I SHALL tell you about a trip that a party of us took down into a coal mine. We went on a very cold day, and as we approached the mine we hastened to a warm place. When we went down into the mine we had a guide go with us for fear we should become lost.

In order to get to the mine proper, we had to go about one hundred feet down a very dark stairway. As we went down the stairway, it grew darker and darker, until finally we had no light except that furnished by some small miners' lamps we had taken to help us find our way after leaving the bright sunlight.

At the bottom of the steps it was very icy and cold; but the guide led us through an open gangway past a door, and here it was much warmer. Then he led us to the rooms where the miners were working.

Perhaps some of you would like to know how they dig coal. They cut it loose at the bottom, between the veins and the slate, by means of a machine; then they bore holes into the coal with a large auger, and in these holes they place gunpowder. When the gunpowder explodes, it breaks down chunks of coal, so that it may be easily shoveled into the cars. After the men touch a lighted match to the powder, they run to the second or third room away to get out of danger of the explosion. When, in a few seconds' time, the powder has exploded, they return to their work.

In these mines they have small dump-cars drawn by one horse. The horses that are used in the mines are well trained; they mind their master so well that he needs no lines with which to guide them. The mines are wired with uncovered wires; and when the horses touch these wires they receive so great a shock that it knocks them down. Miners say this humbles their horses and makes them more obedient. This is pretty hard for the poor horses; nevertheless, they like their work in the mines so well that, having been taken out of the mine for the night, they will run to get back into it the next morning. I wonder how many boys and girls are so anxious to go to their tasks!

In the mines there is one straight track for the cars to run on, and from this track others switch off into the rooms where the miners work. The tracks are double, so an empty car can be brought to the miner on one track while a filled car is taken away on the other. The filled cars are taken to the elevator. This powerful device takes several cars of coal at once up to the surface, where the coal is dumped into larger cars and is ready for market.

We spent several hours in this dark mine, watching the men dig coal. We wondered how the men could endure working there without a ray of sunlight or any good fresh air. Finally we grew tired of walking around in the dark with only the small lamps we had with us to give us light, and decided to return home.

We started up the stairway, and walked and walked; it seemed so long and tiresome. Oh how glad we were when we could see one little ray of sunlight shining through the door as we neared the top! When we reached the door, we were very tired; but we had learned a precious lesson—that of being thankful for the beautiful sunlight and air which we are privileged to enjoy!   —*Mrs. Chas. E. Brown.*

A SEA-TURTLE HUNT

Our Trip to the Gulf

WE LIVED about forty miles from the Gulf of Mexico in the heart of Baldwin County, Alabama. This county is largely a peninsula; Perdido Bay lies to the east, Mobile Bay to the west, and the Gulf of Mexico to the south.

The climate is semitropical, due partly to our proximity to these large bodies of water. Children here never have the pleasure of coasting, skating, sleigh-riding, or snowballing. None of the winter sports of the colder climates are ours; but we have the ever-enjoyable privilege of being out-of-doors nearly every day of the year. And we have some things that afford us pleasure that friends in other sections do not have the privilege of enjoying. Recently we took a very delightful trip. Of this I wish to tell you.

The waters surrounding us teem with many kinds of fish and animal life. Among the living things to be found here is the monstrous animal known as the green sea-turtle. For reasons which I shall give later, we chose to make our trip to the Gulf of Mexico just before the full moon in June. Leaving our home on the Styx River, we made an eight-mile drive by wagon to the home of J. G. Smith, at Loxley, Ala. From there we were to proceed in Mr. Smith's car to the Gulf.

We soon covered the first half of the trip, and arrived at the home of Friend Dreitzler, who, with his wife and son, was to accompany us to the Gulf. Our party now consisted of nine. We separated the party into two divisions. One division, chiefly women, proceeded by car to Orange Beach; the other, men, by hack to Roberts' Landing on Wolf Creek. There we secured a boat, attached the motor, and were soon moving down the creek toward Wolf's Bay, about a seven-mile journey by water, to Orange Beach.

When fairly started, we saw ahead of us a large alligator, perhaps more than fifteen feet in length, crossing the river directly in our course. As we neared him, he sank below the surface and waited for us to pass;

then he again came up and went on his way. The remainder of the trip was uneventful; and, except for the fishes that in great numbers kept popping up out of the water, and for the roughness of the water caused by the wind of an approaching storm, there was nothing to attract our attention and to keep us from enjoying the beauties of the groves and the building sites along the margins of the river and bay.

At the appointed place on Orange Beach we met the others of our party; made arrangements for the night quarters; secured the use of a boat to cross Ornover Bay, which is landlocked; and prepared for our outing on the Gulf Beach. About sunset we were ready to take our bath in the surging, never-quiet Gulf. Real sea-bathing and the sensations it brings to a novice can hardly be described; but they have the "want-more" effect. As darkness approached, we came out of the water and prepared to eat supper. We had brought provisions with us, and some of the women had prepared these and made ready the supper. You may be sure we were all ready for it after spending so strenuous a day.

The beach is at this point exceedingly fine. Stretching back for hundreds of feet from the water's edge, is a wide expanse of fine white sand, nice and clean. Dunes of considerable size resembling huge drifts of snow have been formed. The sand invites you to peaceful repose, and you yield; but you are soon aware, not only that the sea does not rest, but also that the little insects known as sand-fleas will not let you rest. They are tiny creatures and being the color of the sand, evade being seen. But they find you, and bite you, not enough really to hurt, but just enough to annoy you and keep you uneasy.

Your attention will also undoubtedly be drawn to a curious, eight-legged, white-colored creature, perhaps two inches across. It has the ability to run in any direction—backward. forward, right, or left—without turning its body. It seems to be entirely harmless, and is known as the sand-fiddler.

About nine o'clock, the weather having become a little unpleasant, the women of our party recrossed the bay and went to their rest, leaving the men to hunt turtles and to share the fate of the weatherman. Presently the weather changed, and the moon gave nearly full light. This we had wished for; for during the moonlight nights of June the sea-turtles have the habit of coming out of the sea to deposit their eggs in the sand. It is during this time only that they can be found out of their element; and it was our intentions that night to frustrate the plans of some of them.

Catching the Turtles

During these moonlight nights in June, when the turtles leave the water, they are out for only a short period, perhaps never one hour and a half, and many times not so long as that. On coming out, they crawl (you could hardly call the awkward manner of travel walking) to a suitable place on the sand, a distance of seventy-five or more feet from the water, make their nests, and deposit their eggs. The task of one turtle, watched by our party, was performed as follows:

Arriving at a suitable distance from the water, the turtle stopped and began to make her nest. With the forepart of her shell somewhat elevated, with the hinder part she wallowed a few inches into the soft sand; then with the right hind foot, or flipper, she reached directly under the middle and near the rear end of the shell, and took out a quantity of sand and threw it to the right. With the left flipper she reached under the shell in the same manner and threw sand to the left. She repeated with exactness these operations until she had made the hole about seven inches in diameter and two and one-half feet deep, and a little larger at the bottom than at the top.

When the hole was sufficiently finished, she began to deposit her eggs. This required about half an hour. Then she covered the nest so skillfully as to almost defy detection; and it was with some difficulty that we found the eggs, even after we had watched the turtle cover them. The first nest we saw contained 143 eggs; another one we saw contained more than 100. Sometimes more than 200 eggs are deposited at one time.

As the time for us to begin our hunt drew near, we divided our party of four. Then we were ready to patrol the coast and look for "crawls." Two men started down the coast about nine o'clock; the other two, about an hour later. The first two must have started too early, for they walked four or five miles without finding a fresh crawl. My comrade and I had been gone hardly fifteen minutes when we came upon a fresh crawl. Following it about one hundred twenty-five feet, we found a turtle in the act of depositing her eggs. As our presence did not seem to disturb her, we watched her. When she had covered the eggs, she started to return to the water. Then to me was given the pleasure of turning her over on her back; and it took a good, hard lift to do it. When once they are turned on their backs, these turtles are absolutely secure and may be left until you want to return to butcher them.

Leaving that turtle, we moved on down the beach. Soon we found another fresh crawl, and in a few minutes had another turtle placed in the "turned-turtle" position. Shortly after this we met the first two hunters returning. When we told them of our good fortune, they rejoiced with us.

Elated over our night's find, we started for our landing. But fortune favoring us, we found a third turtle just preparing to make her nest. We settled down beside it, and watched the entire procedure. Then Mr. Smith was granted the opportunity of showing it how to "turn turtle."

We now quit the beach, being more than satisfied. In the early gray of the next morning we secured some good sharp knives, hatchets, buckets, and bags of salt, and returned to the beach to butcher the turtles.

The turtle itself is interesting. The one we killed first was a fair sample of the others. It measured about forty inches short diameter, fifty inches long diameter, and thirty inches vertical diameter, and weighed about three hundred pounds, live weight. We cut its head off, removed the lower shell, and skinned and removed the meat, which made about 160 pounds of fine steak. Turtle meat is very palatable to most people; and many like the eggs, though these are tough. Having obtained from one turtle all the meat we desired, we gave the second one to some friends, and released the third, permitting it to go back to the sea. We brought home the upper shell of the one we killed. This shell was so heavy that Mr. Smith and I both became tired carrying it to the boat.

We bade our friends at the shore good-by, and were soon speeding homeward. By sunset we were in our wagon, nearing our own home, which we reached shortly after dark. You should have heard the joyful exclamations of our friends when they beheld the outcome of our good fortune. Many of them want to go turtle-hunting when the season comes again; and we hope to be able to repeat the experience.

—*Chas R. Humble.*

A PLEASANT VISIT TO A CANYON

MAMA and I came out to Grandpa's to stay a few months so Mama could have a good rest in the country. Grandpa lives on a farm in Oklahoma. This farm is a very pleasant, homelike place; and many birds build nests in the grove near the house.

The birds do not seem much afraid of us. There are a pair each of scissortails, mocking-birds, and turtle-doves, all busy finding homes. The mocking-birds wake me up in the morning with their pretty songs. Some quails also are building nests close by, and we often see them in the barn-yard. One evening when a schoolmate and I were crossing a pasture, on our way home, a quail flew up right in front of our faces. She startled us very much, but we found her nest and little eggs. I hear a quail whistling now.

Mama went to see some one who lived quite a distance from our house, and on her way she crossed a deep canyon with high bluffs on each side. She told me about it, and said that some time we must go there for a stroll. The first pleasant Saturday after the weather was warmer, we went.

We arose early and prepared a lunch for dinner. And we took a pail of drinking-water, because we knew the water in the canyon would be bad. We had to walk a mile and a half to get to the canyon.

When we started, we began counting the different varieties of wild flowers, and before the day was ended we had found thirty-three kinds. Mama was surprized that we found so many, for she had guessed there were only twenty kinds. The prairie looked very pretty, covered, as it was, with the many-colored flowers and the soft green grass.

When we arrived at the canyon Mama took me up on a little knoll that was higher than the others and let me look down into the deep place. The bluffs were composed of crumbly, white gypsum; and when I would take up a piece of it, it seemed to have pink streaks in it. It looked very pretty.

The greater part of the canyon was in a pasture, and we had to crawl under a wire fence before we could begin to explore it. Viewing it from the top of the bluff to the little stream at the bottom, the canyon looked to be very deep. But we wished to go to the other side, so we scrambled down the best we could. Our greatest care was for our pail of water; for, if we should spill it, we should have to go thirsty or

drink of the bitter water in the canyon. Once we rested on a ledge of
rocks and let our feet hang down over the edge. When we reached the
bottom of the canyon, I pulled off my shoes and stockings and waded
across the stream, but Mama walked over on some rocks.

Some one had told us that not far from where we were there was
a natural bridge across a side canyon, and we set out to find it. We
looked a long time before we found it, but finally we came to a large
side canyon and followed it till we came to the bridge. It seemed very
wonderful to us that Nature could build a bridge without the aid of
man. This bridge was about twenty-five feet long, and had at one time
been wide enough to permit a team and wagon to cross it; but since then
the sides have crumbled away until now only by careful driving could
one go over it with a buggy. We went down to the bottom of the canyon under the bridge. A nice little stream was flowing there; and it
was very cool, for the breeze blew just right to make it pleasant.

When we were going down, we saw a snake in our path just where
we had to walk. It was lying still, and Mama threw stones at it but
could not hit it. I then tried and hit it on the head. We would have
enjoyed staying there a while had we not seen the snake; but now I
was afraid of everything that moved the grass.

It was not nearly noon yet, but I was very hungry and wanted to
eat; so we began to look for a good place to spread our lunch. I much
desired to find a cave in which to eat our dinner, and we thought we
saw one on the other side, but by the time we had climbed down and
gotten over there, we had lost track of it. Finally we found a beautiful,
shady, mossy dell; and there we ate our dinner.

I still wanted to find a real cave; and so we kept on looking for one.
We went upon the bluff and looked around, and we again saw one on
the other side. We scrambled down and across once more, but lost that
one also. At last, however, we did find one. We had a time climbing
up the hill and through the brush, but when we reached it, we went into
it. It was all in the rock; and there was a spring in the back of the cave,
from which the water flowed into a large pool in the bottom. It was
very nice and cool in there, but we did not stay long.

I was tired by this time and wanted to lie down and rest. I lay
down in a little valley and was almost asleep when I heard Mama singing on the hill above me.

By this time we were both very tired and thirsty; so we stopped at a farm-house close by, where we rested a while and got a good cool drink. We found the wind had risen while we were in the canyon, and to have to face it a mile and a half seemed very hard; but we reached home all right. We thought we had had a very pleasant outing.

—Cleora M. Hale.

THE LIFE OF A SOLDIER

ON June 19, 1916, when President Wilson called for men, I decided to enlist to serve my country for a period of three years, the length of time every one who enlists must serve. On June 28th, at Ft. Myer, Va., I went to enlist. There we were taught the first steps taken in making a man into a fighting unit. When I went to the recruiting-officer to enlist, I met my first surprize. Not every one is taken. A young man must show the record of a good character, have some education, and be in good health; he is closely examined on these points.

After passing the examination, I was accepted, and told to stand at "attention" and take the oath of allegiance—that every man enlisting must take. Then I was given my uniform, etc., for a soldier has to have many things—some he does not know what to do with at first. But it does not take him long to learn their uses, and then they become his necessities.

I was assigned to a company consisting of about seventy enlisted men, and three commissioned officers—the captain and first and second lieutenants. My first few days were hard ones, for I had to learn many things I did not know that a soldier had to know—how to march in various ways and how to take the different steps. This took nearly a week. Then I was given a rifle, the pride of every man when he first enlists. After this came the real work. I had to learn what is called the Manual of Arms; we were taught how to carry our rifles, how to salute, and how to go through many other drills, which space will not allow me to explain.

Finally the drill-sergeant told me I should enter ranks with the older men. I was then put into a squad consisting of eight men. There are nine such squads in my company, and each squad is in charge of a corporal. The men of lowest rank are called privates; then come the non-commissioned officers, consisting of corporals and sergeants; then the commissioned officers, including those from a second lieutenant of a company to a general of an army in time of war; and finally the commander-in-chief, who at present is President Wilson. A soldier has to learn all of these and their different ranks, about thirteen important grades, and some of these are subdivided, especially the ranks of the non-commissioned officers.

Judging from my own experience, drill and discipline, including team-work, are the factors that make our army what it is. There are many kinds of drills, but all are classed under two headings, close-order drills and extended-order drills. The next time you see soldiers passing you rank after rank and file by file, remember they are on close-order parade. Extended-order parade you may never see, for the soldiers are taught this for use only in time of war. It is then that team-work counts. Before playing baseball or football, a team gets together and practises so that it may win in a real contest. Soldiers do the same; they have to get together and practise in order to be able, when war breaks out, to protect our homes and mothers, sisters and children, wives and friends, from an enemy that would destroy our homes and country. We can work together that we may win, and keep in safety all that we love; but, in the great war-games that are played, many boys fall, never to return after the battle is fought and won.

Discipline comes through long-continued drills and subordination. I found it hard at first; but, as time has passed I have become accustomed to it, and have learned what obedience means. Sometimes one is almost ready to think that his officers are very hard on him, but work has to be done. A soldier has to do many things besides learn to fight or make a fine showing in parade. There are times when, after drills, I desire to take a good rest; but there are other things to do. Sometimes there are trenches to be dug, wood to be cut, clothes to be washed; and, unlike it is at home, we have to wash our own clothes and mend them. There is one thing the soldier must do; he must keep himself clean and his equipment in order. Many are punished for not obeying on this line. We have to take a bath every other day, and keep all our dishes and metal equipment spotless, especially our rifles, for they are inspected every day.

Each day men are taken from the company to do other work, such as helping in the kitchen; it is no light work to cook for seventy men three times a day. And aside from the kitchen details, there is other work to be done; but the men on those details do not drill that day. The men are changed every day, so as to even up the work and allow each man to have a chance at drills. I have told you of only a few things that a soldier has to do and know. To one who has never been in the service, it may look as if a soldier has it easy, and many of us do part of the time, for it is not always that we have to work hard.

We have a certain routine for the day. At 6:30 is reveille, when the morning report is made. Then comes physical exercise, after which we have breakfast, or morning mess. After mess comes fatigue, or police duty, when the company has to clean up the company's street, clean out the tents, make the beds, and get ready for drill. We are given about two hours for this work, then we drill until eleven. Then we have an hour to rest and to get ready for dinner, or noon mess. In the afternoon we seldom have to drill, and so this gives us time to rest, and to do our washing, mending, etc. Generally our captain talks to us for an hour about our drills or about our taking care of ourselves. At 5 P. M. we have supper, or, as we call it, mess; all three meals we call the same name.

After supper comes retreat, when the buglers give the Call to Colors, the band plays our national hymn, and the first sergeant of our company reads the evening report, or the roll-call, to see that every man is in camp. After that we can go out of camp, if we wish, until ten o'clock. At nine the Call to Quarters is sounded; then all visitors are to leave, and the men are to keep quiet so that those who wish to retire may do so and not have their rest disturbed. At ten all lights must be out, and every soldier in bed. A soldier in the field needs all the rest and sleep he can get, for he has hard work to perform the next day.

Whether a man enjoys or endures life in the army, depends on the man himself. He can make it easy or hard, according as he obeys or disobeys. By doing what he is told to do without finding fault, by living right and not breaking the laws laid down to govern the company, a man can make army life much easier. Of course, if a soldier disobeys, he suffers for it, either by doing extra work or by losing his liberty; and, in case it becomes necessary, a man is court-martialed, that is, he is tried by a court of officers and, if found guilty, is sentenced to the guard-house and fined as a man would be if he had broken civil laws.

We are given good food; it is not, however, just what we would get at home, for there are no pies, cakes, and sweets. Each of us is allowed twenty-nine cents a day for rations; for extra rations each one gives his captain one dollar a month on every pay-day.

The pay of a soldier, when he enlists as a private, is fifteen dollars a month, cash. It does not look like much; but then we buy no clothes or shoes out of that, for we have a clothing allowance on which we draw. If a man is careful of his clothing and draws only what he needs, so that when he is discharged he has not drawn out all of his allowance, he then draws the balance in cash. Besides, we have no board to pay, and medical attention is free. If one becomes sick, he is compelled to go to the hospital right after breakfast when the sick-call is given. This is a good thing; for if the sick were not looked after promptly, just think what might happen in a camp of fifteen hundred men if one man should take a contagious disease. Only the best doctors are in the United States military service.

After spending nearly four months at Fort Myer, Va., we were ordered to the border, and went to Ft. Sam Houston, Tex. We left Washington, D. C., at midnight on a troop-train of eighteen cars, and for five days traveled south. When we arrived at Ft. Sam Houston, we were glad to get out of the cars. The first thing we did was to pitch our tents and get settled in our new quarters, after which we ate our dinners. Then for two days we did little. But after this we began drilling again. Drilling on the hot plains of Texas was different from drilling on the cool hills of Virginia. But a soldier's home is where he is sent; so he has to be contented.

That you may get some idea of our daily work, or drill, I shall take you through one of the extended-order drills, which are nearly all alike. We have finished our morning work and are waiting for the bugle-call. First comes First Call. Each soldier puts on his cartridge-belt, to which it attached a bayonet, a first-aid pack, and sometimes a canteen, a water-flask used for carrying water to drink. We take our rifles and fall in, that is, we line up for a roll-call. The first sergeant takes charge of the company; then the order Squads Right, Forward March is given, and sixty-odd men execute the order as one man, and march to the drill-grounds.

Then comes the bayonet-drill. The bayonet is a sword-knife, which fastens over the muzzle of the rifle. One edge is a cutting-blade, nearly sixteen inches long. The back has what is called a false edge, which runs the whole length of the bayonet. This bayonet weighs one pound, and is used in close fighting when rifle-fire can not be used or when the enemy has to be driven out of a trench or position which he is holding. It is said that in a bayonet charge the attacked party seldom remains to dispute the question as to whether or not they should attempt to hold the position or trench; and I hardly blame them, for in just a drill, to lie in a trench and see a mob of men coming toward you on the run with fixed bayonets, and yelling as if they were going to run the knives through you, which in actual warfare they would do, causes you to experience unpleasant feelings.

After drilling with the bayonet, we march nearly two miles from camp for extended-order drill. We are in company formation, or marching order. After carrying out a series of orders, such as Squads Left, Half, and Rest, we sit down or lie down and rest, while the officers and non-commissioned officers talk out the plans for the drill. When they have these settled, we are called to attention and made to lie down; sometimes we must lie in cactus-thorns, dirt, or dust. Whenever an order to lie down is given, down you must lie, no matter where you are.

The range of fire given is generally eight hundred yards. When we get into position and get into range, then comes the order Fire at Will. All that can be heard is the rattle of rifle-fire. It is almost impossible to hear vocal orders, so the officers use whistles and army signals. The whistles blow, we are ordered to fire faster; then we see on our right a squad of men rush forward a short distance, drop to the ground, and open fire. Squad after squad rushes up the same way. Our corporal shouts, "Cease firing; load and lock; prepare to rush"; then we dig our right foot into the ground, hold the rifle in our hands, rise on our left elbow, and draw the left leg up under us, ready to spring. It takes only a few seconds to execute all this. "Follow me," calls the corporal; and we spring up and run, keeping low to the ground, so that if we were in real war we should stand a less chance of being shot. When we arrive on the new line, we lie down and again open fire. In this way we cover ground to get nearer to the enemy. When the opposing rifle-fire becomes too strong, we fix bayonets and rush to the trench to chase out the opposers. If we can not chase them out, we have to dig into the ground and make a trench for ourselves. In this drill we go through just the same things we would in actual war.

One day my squad was ordered to move forward to hold a position. On arriving, we found a natural hole in the ground covered with cactus.

In order to lie down with comfort I used the butt of my rifle to knock down some earth to cover the cactus, and, in so doing I found a nest of scorpions. I killed nine, some of the other boys killed the rest; and we lay down out of sight, trusting that we should come out all right without being stung. Many times the boys have to kill rattlesnakes in order to obey orders.

Many times I have had to crawl on my hands and knees through brush in order to find the enemy's position; and it is not an easy task to lie motionless a long time in order to keep from being caught and made a prisoner. This kind of work is called scouting, and all the cunning and art of the Indian warfare has to be used. A scout has to find as many as he can of the enemy, and give the information to his comrades; so he has to be very careful not to get caught. If he is caught, his failure may mean a victory lost and many men killed.

Obedience and sacrifice go together in war. I never knew what it is to obey until lately, though I thought I knew. But when some officer calls a soldier from the ranks and orders him to do a duty that means almost certain death, he has to obey and ask no questions. If he returns to his comrades, he has done well; if not, it is only the sacrifice of one life that others might live. "To obey is better than sacrifice," is a good motto, and is often used by us, as there are times in a soldier's life when to obey means to sacrifice his own life.

It is not often that an officer will sacrifice his men; our officers do all they can to save us. But lower officers must obey their superiors, the same as we must obey ours, and if superior officers deem it necessary to give an order, our officers must obey even if they know that to do so will mean a sacrifice of their men.

The man in the army who has it easy, is promoted, and receives the better pay, is the one who obeys, studies to please his officers, learns the lessons of the different drills, and behaves himself. But the one who thinks he would have an easier life than he is having at home is mistaken; for here you have to work and work hard. At the same time, however, it gives a young man a confidence in himself that he would hardly get without military training.

Companions are not all of the best; some will drink, gamble, and wreck their manhood. But please do not blame the army; for a soldier, when he is off duty, has time to do as he pleases, and, if he chooses to drink, gamble, and commit ungodly acts, and thereby wreck his manhood, it is his own fault. He is given every chance to make a man of himself; and if he will study and learn, he may win promotion.

A young man in the military service has the same chance to "make good" as he would have in civil life, if not a better chance; for he is more closely watched. He has to be in at a certain time, unless he has permission from his captain to be out; he has to learn to take care of himself, except when he is sick; and he is restricted and punished by work or imprisonment if he becomes intoxicated or gets into some trouble.

By keeping everything clean and orderly, I get about six or eight hours for rest during the day, besides eight hours for sleep during the night. On Sunday work is assigned to none except those who must be in the kitchen, and their work is made as light as possible. Those who wish to go to church have that privilege.

Saturday is the weekly inspection-day; then all clothing and equipment are examined. When inspection-day comes we make sure we have everything done; for otherwise we shall be given extra work to do. The inspecting is done in the forenoon; the rest of the day, as well as Sunday, we have to ourselves.

What I have written gives you some insight into the life of the soldier.
—*C. H. Lewis.*

A DOUBLE RESCUE

THE tall chalk cliffs along the northeastern coast of France are, on the average, about three hundred feet high. They are steep, and some even overhang their base. The narrow beach is not composed of sand but of flinty stones, and the waves break upon it with great power.

At some places along the beach a certain species of seaweed grows which is valued by the French peasants as a fertilizer. But a difficulty lay in getting it above the cliffs. To overcome this trouble they invented a simple little device. At the summit of the cliff was placed a cylinder, over this was placed a long stout rope. One end hung over the cliff and had a basket fastened to it. To the other end a donkey or horse was hitched. Two peasants worked at the machine. One filled the basket with the seaweed, and the other led the horse. When the horse started on its trip inland, the basket steadily rose from the beach to the top of the cliff, where it was emptied. Then it was lowered for another load. In this way about twenty-five basketfuls could be taken up in a day. The signal for hauling the basket up was a shake of the rope; for the man above seldom troubled himself to look over the edge, but passed the time while the basket was being filled lying on his back smoking his pipe. He usually lay with his head on the rope so he could readily tell when the signal was given.

That you may understand the story that I am about to tell you, you must know of another feature peculiar to this cliff. This was the smugglers' stairway—a rude, spiral stairway tunneled in the cliff itself, mounting up in irregular windings from the beach to the summit. It was lighted at intervals by windows or doors—openings of different sizes and of irregular forms, cut through the front of the precipice. It was a tiresome climb in summer; and those who made the ascent were glad to stop at the openings to rest and to take a look out over the blue sea.

It happened that one of the little devices of which I have spoken was placed directly over this stairway, and the rope hung down in front of it. The brow of the cliff projected at this place, and so the rope hung out about ten feet from the openings of the stairway.

Now the story. Mr. H. was spending the summer at Fecamp, a little village inhabited by fishermen and farmers. A few folk from Paris and England, who desired rest and seclusion, chose this place as a resort. It was not at all fashionable, but the bathing was good and the scenery fine.

Mr. H. made the acquaintance of a very pretty child, the three-year-old daughter of a fisherman who cultivated a little patch of land above the cliff when he was not engaged in fishing. The little girl's ways were as pretty as she was herself. She wore dresses to her knees, and her brown feet and legs and her curly head were bare. Mr. H. met her on the beach, where she amused herself while her mother was gathering seaweed for her husband, who was up on the cliff with the horse. Mr. H. liked Nannette the first time he saw her, and they became comrades forthwith. He loved to stroll along the beach and to play with his little friend.

Mr. H. had another friend at Fecamp, who was quite different from Nannette. He was a boy of sixteen, a fine manly-looking chap, blue-eyed and fair-haired. He was lovable, modest, and well-bred. But his history was very sad. His father and mother were dead. His mother had been a slave to the drink-habit. He inherited plenty of money, but also the tendency to drink. Poor boy! He would be overcome by the insane longing for drink. His friends tried all the remedies they knew of, but to no avail. When in his normal state, he earnestly helped in all efforts to cure him; but when the dark hour came, he was another creature. His home was in Rugby, England. His good aunt had brought him to Fecamp, thinking the pure air and strange surroundings would help him.

Mr. H. took an interest in this unfortunate boy, whom we shall call Robert. They were much together, and he tried to help the boy all he could. One day as they were strolling down the beach, on their way to have a little visit with Nannette, Mr. H. noticed that Robert wore a gloomy look. He knew the dark fit was coming on. He tried to divert the boy's mind to something else, but succeeded only in part. Robert's face was the picture of despair. He loathed himself. He wanted deliverance, but knew not how to get it. He had, the best he knew how, asked God to help him. As they approached Nannette and her mother, the latter paused to give them a grin of welcome, and Nannette trotted stumblingly up to them and put her hand in Robert's. He stooped down and kissed the girl's face repeatedly. Then suddenly he straightened up again and said, "I'm not fit to touch her."

All at once an idea came to the mind of Mr. H. (Might not Providence have inspired it?), and he addressed Robert thus: "Look here, have you ever tried how quick you could go up the smugglers' staircase? I'll wager you can't get to the top in ten minutes. Come—let's see what you can do for the honor of Rugby! Off you go, now! I'll hold the watch on you. One minute to three: you have a minute to reach the foot of the stairs, and start on the even hour. Lively!"

Anything to make him forget himself. Robert probably understood his friend's motive. But be that as it may, he decided against his gloomy, despondent feelings, took a full breath, and started off. "Good!" thought Mr. H. "By the time he's at the top of that cliff, there won't be enough of him left to think of whisky." Mr. H. sat down, leaned against a rock, and prepared to observe the ascent. Robert would come into view as he passed one of the openings.

Nannette, surprised at Robert's sudden departure, gazed at him till he disappeared within the cliff and then resumed her work of helping mother. She would pick up a scrap of seaweed between her tiny thumb and finger and put it in the basket, which was two thirds full. Just at this time her mother was some distance away gathering a large armful of the brown glistening stuff, which had been rolled up by the surf. The sea was blue and calm; yet a heavy surf was breaking on the beach, causing a softly thunderous sound. From out of an almost clear sky the afternoon sun was shining against the white face of the cliff. In the heart of that cliff was a young soul toiling upward for freedom. "God bless him," prayed Mr. H., "and give him deliverance!"

Robert passed the first opening about sixty feet from the base, without even turning to look at his friend. The next opening was over one hundred feet above. Mr. H. sat, with his open watch in his hand, deeply thinking. All at once he was aroused by a loud scream. It was so piercing and agonizing that it instantly brought him to his feet. What he saw filled him with horror.

The mother of Nannette had uttered the scream, and was now running in great excitement toward the basket. The basket was no longer on the beach; it had begun its journey upward, and was already ten feet from the ground. And Nannette was in it! The child had managed to clamber into the basket, and in doing so had shaken the rope in such a way that her father had taken it for the usual signal and had started the horse. Of course he did not know that his little daughter was in the basket.

Nannette was in grave danger. She might fall out before she reached the top; but if she did not, she surely would when the basket tipped to go over the edge of the cliff. There was no way of getting at her nor of letting her father know what was happening. Mr. H. ran to the distracted mother. As he was running, he stripped off his thin, summer coat and made her understand that they would hold it, and if possible, catch Nannette when she should fall. But they stood only a small chance of catching the child, for the basket swung to and fro as it went steadily up.

Nannette's face appeared and disappeared over the edge of the basket. Should they tell her to jump? It would be dangerous for her to do so. But the higher she went, the less likely would she be to escape alive. Should she stay in the basket until it reached the summit of the cliff and be pitched out by the turning over of the basket, she would certainly be killed. It could not be hoped that she would survive a fall of three hundred feet; but there was nothing to be done but to stand and await the issue.

Just then, however, an unexpected thing happened. Nannette's deadly peril had caused Robert to be forgotten; but just at this moment he appeared at the second opening. You remember that the rope was hanging in front of the openings, but a distance of ten feet away. The basket with Nannette in it was only twelve feet below this opening. Robert had not much time to think, but it was evident from his actions that he intended to jump for the basket. He must not jump into the basket, for that would tip it and throw Nannette out. There was scarcely room enough in it for both of them at best. He must aim to catch the rope a little above the basket and then let himself down into it. Then, too, he must wait till the basket was nearly on a level with him so his weight would not cause too great a shock when he would catch the rope. But could he leap ten feet horizontally from a standing take-off and catch the rope? and that just after having tried his strength to the utmost in racing up those steps?

With his arms outstretched Robert leaped forward, lightly and boldly into the air. It seemed to Mr. H., who was in almost breathless suspense, that Robert hung a long time in space, though it was all done in a fraction of a second. Robert caught the rope. Then, hand under hand, he lowered himself into the basket and put his arm around Nannette's waist. The mother was frantic with joy. She hardly knew how to give vent to her feelings.

The basket ceased to ascend. The sudden jerk of the rope doubtless caused the father to wonder what was the matter. Anyway, his head and shoulders were presently seen over the edge of the cliff. Then he vanished, and soon the basket with its precious contents began slowly to descend. In a few minutes more Nannette was in her mother's arms, and Robert and Mr. H. were shaking hands. Robert was quiet, but he looked very happy. The melancholy gloom that had been overshadowing him only a few minutes before had now entirely disappeared.

He had been under the terror and despair of his dark hour, all his thoughts and emotions centered upon himself; but the opportunity to hazard his life for the sake of another had, he felt convinced, proceeded straight from heaven. He had been enabled to forget himself at the right time, had won a victory for himself, and had saved a precious little life—a double rescue.

We may learn from this forceful example to forget ourselves and gain victories over self by doing something for others who are in greater need than we are ourselves. Robert later had some struggles; but he had no more of those dark hours of despair. He became an officer in India, did many heroic deeds, and was beloved by his men.

A TRIP UP THE HUDSON

IN striking contrast with the activity and commotion of life in New York City is the delightful quiet of a ride on the smooth, placid waters of the Hudson. Since it is perhaps the most popular waterway in the world, this American Rhine needs no introduction. It abounds in beauty of natural scenery, and flows through a section of country rich in historical association. On its very banks have occurred many events that have become a part of our country's history.

The river was named after Henry Hudson, by whom it was explored, in 1609, as far as Albany. On this river Robert Fulton, in 1807, demonstrated that a vessel can be successfully propelled by steam, when his boat, the Clermont, made the voyage from New York to Albany. It was on the shore of the Hudson that Washington Irving lived and wrote his legends. It was he who, perhaps more than any other man, made the world acquainted with its beauty, and who said, "I thank God I was born on the banks of the Hudson."

Let us take one of the large, elegant steamers of the Hudson River Day Line, three of which are named in honor of the three prominent persons just mentioned. It happens that today our boat will be the Washington Irving, the largest and newest of the fleet. She has a capacity for, and has a license to carry, 6,000 people—the largest license ever issued by any government. Everything that safety, speed, and comfort require is provided for in her construction and equipment, and her interior is decorated with many paintings representative of Irving's life and writings. On going aboard, we find that there is a room where coats and parcels and such things may be checked free, so we need not carry these about; and also that there is a restaurant where we may supplement our lunch if we so desire.

Our vessel steams away from the pier, and we are at once on our voyage up the Hudson. The river is wide. Its volume is far out of proportion to its drainage area, due to the fact that in recent geological time the Hudson Valley has sunk considerably causing it to be "drowned." And also the tide from the ocean causes a reversal of the stream, the effect being noticeable as far up the river as Albany.

We note on either side of the river the great transatlantic liners lying at their docks. The towering buildings of lower Manhattan begin to appear as grouped together in an immense cluster. But let us now for a few hours turn our attention ahead and note the panorama that lines both sides of the river. The orchestra has started to play.

Grant's tomb makes a striking appearance on the east bank. On the west is the site of the Hamilton-Burr duel. We pass the promontory on which Fort Washington was located, and also, directly opposite, on the New Jersey side, the site of Fort Lee, the place from which General Washington witnessed, in 1776, the bloody capture of Fort Washington by the British, in one of the fiercest conflicts of the Revolution.

By this time we notice the west bank has become a perpendicular cliff that rises from the water's edge to a height of from three hundred to five hundred feet. This is the far-famed Palisades which occupy about fifteen miles of the river's shore-line. Here we see hardy trees and shrubs that have found scanty lodgment in the steep sides and are trying their best to grow in their natural way.

Soon we enter the broad Tappan Zee, where the river expands to a width of three miles. Sunnyside, the residence of Irving, may be seen nestled among the trees. Near Tarrytown is the little valley that Irving has immortalized by his Legend of Sleepy Hollow. Here, in Sleepy Hollow Cemetery, Irving is buried. It was near Tarrytown also that Major Andre was captured, in 1780, by three American militiamen. Farther up the river we pass the point on the west bank where Andre landed for a conference with Benedict Arnold in regard to surrendering to the British, West Point, where nearly all the stock of the Americans' ammunition was stored. Passing Stony Point, we recall that it was here that Mad Anthony Wayne performed the brilliant feat of capturing the British position.

Now we come to a narrower portion of the river, the gateway to the Highlands, "where every mountain had its beacon fires of liberty and every promontory its patriotic fortifications." The Highlands rise to an elevation of fifteen hundred feet, and the river winds through them in a picturesque gorge. Have the kodak ready, for we shall obtain some beautiful views.

On the east bank, high above the river, are the buildings of the West Point military academy. Surely a more delightful location could not have been chosen, for there is something about the air and the water and the scenery here that is indescribably grand.

As our steamer moves steadily upstream we pass Newburgh, an old German settlement. At Poughkeepsie we glide under the high bridge. Soon the Catskills, where Rip Van Winkle slept, are visible in the distance. Both Kingston and Catskill are gateways to this vacation-land. We pass Hudson, once a whaling port, on the east bank. Finally, at the end of our journey, we reach Albany, with its 23,000,000-dollar capitol and other places of interest.

We reflect that what impressed us most on our 150-mile trip was, not the interest attaching to the places on the shore, but the charm of the scenery—the delightfulness of the trip itself. —*A. L. Byers.*

OUR TRIP TO THE BEES' NEST

ONE day the children's uncle noticed some bees taking water from the river. As bees usually fly in a direct line from the water to the nest, he followed them some distance in order to learn where their nest was. Finally he noticed bees buzzing around one of the upper limbs of a large box-tree growing on our lease-land, about a mile and a half from home. When he told us about it, we concluded there would be a good-sized nest of bees in the tree, and that in about three months' time we should have a considerable quantity of honey.

When the three months were about ended, Father and Uncle suggested that we go to the nest and get the honey. We were soon ready. Aunty and her three children were here on a visit. We were a party of eleven. We took a bucket, a small tub to put the honey in, and a large knife and spoon to handle it with. We had a little trouble in finding the tree, as there were so many alike. But when we had found it, we sat down on a log some distance away, charging Jimmy, the aboriginal (This occurred in Australia.), to tend the horses while Father and Uncle chopped the tree down.

As soon as it had fallen, Father tried to enclose the opening of the nest (or hive) as much as possible, but he was not quite quick enough. Some of the bees, enraged at the disturbance, attacked him very savagely. He ran and the bees followed. He would throw himself on the ground at intervals, and they would fly over him; but when he would rise, they would again attack him, and he received many stings about the head and hands. Finally they left him. But there was some excitement for a short time, and the horses became so frightened that Jimmy could scarcely hold them. In the meantime Uncle had been busying himself making fires near the tree, for in smoke the bees are not nearly so savage. The smoke makes them drowsy, seeming to numb their senses to a certain extent.

Some chopping now had to be done to make the opening large enough to get at the honey. After a while we ventured up to the tree to have a look, taking care that a stray bee did not light on us. There, embedded in the hollow of the tree, lay in long layers, about six rows of beautiful white comb, the wax cells full of good honey. Father took some of the honeycomb out and placed it on a piece of clean bark that served as a plate. Then we went back to our seat on the log to eat our honey. We could not eat much, for it was so sweet. We all enjoyed it, however, especially the children.

When all the honeycomb had been taken out of the "hive," we left for home pleased with the outing and with the quantity of honey obtained. When the honey was strained out, we had about sixty pounds. The wax was boiled down and strained. Then it set firm, and we found it useful for many things.   —*Isabella Raines.*

INTERESTING CLIMBS ON MACKINAC ISLAND

WHEN we left the Mission House, we walked along the eastern-shore drive. On the one side was the water, on the other were the steep cliffs. We walked along, admiring the wooded slopes, until we came to a spring, where we quenched our thirst with the excellent water.

On the steep slopes grew evergreen trees—cedar, spruce, and balsam. At some places they seemed to grow out of the very rocks themselves. Of course, these trees were stunted, but we wondered at their growing at all. The slopes on the southwestern shore, which we had seen the day before, were more thickly wooded than those of the eastern shore. They were indeed very beautiful.

We climbed some steep places. One of these was on the western shore. We thought we could get a fine view from the top, so we started up. It was a more difficult climb than we had expected. The hardest place was near the summit. It looked as if we could not reach the top; but after we had worked so hard and had come so far, we would not be baffled by this last difficulty. We were determined to reach the top, and we did so. Once at the summit, we looked down and were surprized

when we saw what a steep place we had ascended. But the beautiful view we had was well worth the climb.

In the Christian way there are some steep places to climb. The trials may seem hard, it may look as if we could go no farther; but if we will be determined to conquer and will persevere, we shall gain the victory. God will not suffer us to fail, if we do our part. And we shall not be sorry that we have gone through the trial, but shall rejoice over the good things we have received through it.

But I must return to my story about our walk on the eastern shore.

After we left the spring, we continued our walk along the shore until we came to Arch Rock, which you see in the picture. The summit of this natural bridge is one hundred and forty-nine feet above the level of the lake. From the top to the base of the arch it is forty-nine feet. Part way down the steep descent are smaller arch rocks. We passed through one called Fairy Arch. This, however, was much smaller than the one in the picture.

We climbed up to the edge of the bridge. Should we walk across? It was rugged and quite narrow, more narrow than the picture shows it to be. Indeed, it is so slender that as early as seventy-five years ago some visitors thought it would soon fall. Also there was danger of our falling off. We looked out over the stretching waters of Lake Huron. We dimly saw in the distance a number of islands. After admiring the grandeur of the scene for a time, we became courageous enough to cross the arch.

After leaving Arch Rock, we followed a drive through beautiful forests until we came to this huge conical rock. (See the picture.) It is called Sugar Loaf, and was believed by the Indians to be the abode of his god.

It seems strange that a single great rock like this should be found in the midst of a forest. The rock is ninety feet high. It is broken with crevices and cracks, which give lodgment for scanty vegetation, which springs from seeds brought by the wind and birds. The steps you see lead to a little cave. Fissures branch off from it and extend throughout the rock. In this little cave we found the names of many visitors written on the rock.

We descended the steps and walked round the great loaf. We wished we might be at the top, but thought it an impossibility to make the ascent. But we became venturesome, and up the rock we started. Crevices in the rock and some little scrubby trees aided us, and we reached the very summit of Sugar Loaf.

Other visitors who had come to see this natural wonder were surprized to see us at the top. Some remained to see whether we should get down safely. For a moment we ourselves were fearful. We knew that making the descent would be more difficult than making the ascent. But we took courage and started. We went slowly and carefully; for we knew that, if we should lose our hold, the result would be serious. We found that when we looked down to the base and thought of the dangerous descent we became more fearful; so we avoided looking down and looked up instead.

What an apt illustration this is of the way we should do in our Christian experience! We should look up to Jesus, for in him we find encouragement and grace for every need.

We reached the base of the rock safely, and felt thankful to God for his protection.

—*Bessie L. Byrum.*

LOST IN THE JUNGLE

ONE year I decided to spend my two-weeks' vacation in southern Alabama and Florida. Leaving Pittsburg on a Tuesday morning in May, a friend and I reached our farm about twenty miles west of Pensacola, Florida, Wednesday night. On Saturday evening, after having worked very hard during the three preceding days, we decided to go fishing, knowing that the streams there abounded with fish. Shortly after dark we arrived at the fishing-place in the Black Water River, about a mile and a half distant from our camp. After fishing for half an hour with no success, we decided to return home; and just then our trouble began.

We started, we supposed, in the right direction for home, but we had not gone far until we realized that we were off the track. We then tried to locate the place where we had been fishing, but could not with any certainty. Everything was dark before us, and we soon found ourselves in a swamp. Supposing that, if we were to cross this swamp, we should be able to find something we could recognize, we crossed it, only to find that there was nothing familiar in sight. After tramping through strange territory for a while longer, we awoke to the fact that we were lost in the swamps, and we began to wonder when we should be able to locate ourselves and find our home.

We tramped through almost impenetrable swamps and jungles of underbrush, now stopping to gaze at the face of the sky, hoping thus to tell in which direction we were going, now examining the bark of the trees; in fact, we tried every plan of which we had ever heard or read whereby we might find out, if possible, where we were and in what direction we were going. No familiar scenes greeted our sight; no sounds could be heard except the cries of the night-birds, the croak of the bullfrogs, and the murmur of the breezes among the pines. No lights could be seen except those made by the thousands of fireflies flitting here and there; and these served only to deceive us, for now and again we mistook one of these flitting things for a light borne by some one, and our hope would rise only to fall, on our learning that it was but a firefly.

Finally it dawned on our minds that we were in deadly peril. Here we were, perhaps five miles from human habitation, in the heart of a great swamp and dense jungle which, very probably, was never before penetrated by human being. These swamps were infested and alive with the deadly moccasin, the bite of which meant certain death. They were also the home of the alligator. The dense jungle afforded shelter for the bear; and we were liable at any moment to come upon an old mother bear and her cubs. More terrifying than all these, if such were possible, was the knowledge that we were right in the midst of the treacherous quick-sands, from whose clutches we could never hope to escape should we once be caught. Our position was critical in the extreme.

For five long hours we tramped through this swamp, turning this way and that; penetrating thick underbrush through which we were unable to see five feet ahead of us; often sinking into the swamp and mire to our knees, going down with a dull "chug"; not knowing at what moment we might tramp on the deadly moccasin and thus end our journey.

We knew that there was an old tram-road west of our house, and that if we could only find this road, we could find our home. But our search for it was fruitless. We tried to find our way to the river, and finally succeeded; but because of the impenetrable underbrush and marshes along its banks, we could not

follow it with any certainty. Besides, the river was forty to sixty feet deep, the night was dark, and the banks were abrupt; and we were in danger at every step of being precipitated into the dark waters. So we gave up the plan of following the river.

About midnight we came to a point where the white sand had been washed out in a pile, and here we considered the advisability of camping for the night. Our clothing was soaked with perspiration, our feet and legs were water-soaked, our shoes were filled with mud and slime from the swamp, our toes were blistered, our feet were swollen, and we were utterly exhausted. After our five-hour tramp through the jungle, we found this spot to be inviting. Here we could at least build a fire, and by its light could see that the place was free from snakes. But before finally deciding to take this step, we called as loudly as we could and listened intently for a sound, but we received no answer. We supposed we were probably five miles from home; and who in that forest country would be awake at that hour of the night? "But see! there is a light. Some one must be searching for us." My companion's wife was at the house, and would not go to sleep until she knew of our whereabouts; perhaps this was her beacon-light. But no; it was only a firefly flitting through the air. There was no hope of reaching home that night. We made our fire around an old pine-stump; and clad in our wet garments, with no cover but the sky above us, we lay down and after breathing a silent prayer to God to protect us as he had done thus far, we went to sleep. We wakened often, replenished our fire, gazed out into the impenetrable darkness and still wondered where we were. We had not had a drink of water since six o'clock the evening before, and our throats and tongues were parched. The river was near us, but to attempt to get water from it was hazardous. We must pass the night without water, though surrounded by it.

About four o'clock in the morning we saw Halley's comet, and by it we knew that we were west of our home; but it was yet too dark for us to attempt to find our way out. At daylight, however, we resumed our long search for home; and after we had walked about half a mile, our eyes caught sight of our house, the goal for which we had tramped five weary hours and away from which we had spent that long, fearful night.

From this harrowing experience I learned several valuable moral lessons. While we were tramping through this swamp and jungle, my companion went ahead and carried the lantern, because he had high boots through which a snake could not bite. I felt that my greatest safety lay in stepping in his footsteps; and this I did, following so closely that I scarcely missed a step. This forcibly impressed on my mind the necessity of our walking in the footsteps of Jesus if we wish to be protected from harm. It also came to my mind vividly that Paul was at one time stranded on an island among a strange people, where a deadly snake fastened itself upon him and he shook it off and was not injured, though the natives looked for him to fall dead at any moment. In our peril I thought, "If I could only have the faith of Paul, that in case one of those deadly snakes should bite me, it could do me no harm!" and I secretly breathed a prayer to the great God of heaven that he would give me that faith.

When we reached home and found that we had camped only a short distance from there, and that my companion's wife had heard our cries, and, supposing they were ours, had tried to signal us; and found also that she had spent a sleepless night, fearing to go out into the thicket and yet unable to sleep for anxiety, I was reminded that many thousands of people are near their eternal home, and yet may be lost, not hearing or seeing the welcoming signal of their friends who are making frantic efforts to direct them to the haven of rest.

I had not felt so happy for a long time as I felt when we emerged from that thicket and saw before us our "home, sweet home."

—A. T. Rowe.